A NEW LIFE PROMISE

HOW TO HEAL YOUR BODY, FIND JOY, AND BRING GLORY TO GOD

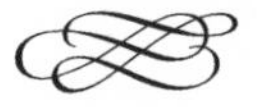

ISABEL D. PRICE

Paperback ISBN: 979-8-9853208-0-0

Ebook ISBN: 979-8-9853208-1-7

This book was developed with Laura Gale. You can find out more about producing a book of your own at www.lauraiswriting.com

CONTENTS

PART I
A NEW LIFE PROMISE

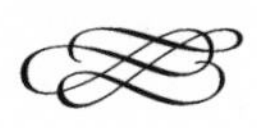

INTRODUCTION

> "For I know the plans I have for you," declares the Lord, "plans to prosper you and not to harm you, plans to give you hope and a future.
>
> — JEREMIAH 29:11

~

If I were to ask you to honestly describe yourself, what would you say?

Would you describe yourself as God sees you — beautiful, beloved, perfect in His eyes?

Or would you use the harsh words that flood your mind when you look in the mirror? Words like 'fat', 'a disappointment', or even something as unkind as 'disgusting'?

If the words that came to mind to describe yourself were the cruel ones you say to yourself on a daily basis, this book is for you.

My name is Isabel. We don't know each other yet, but I

hope that will change in the coming months. You see, this book is an invitation. Through my work as a nutritionist, God has called me to help Christian women who are struggling with their weight to find their light again. My prayer for you is that this book will help you learn to heal your body from the inside out, so that hope for your future returns, and so you can live in the joy that is your birthright as a child of God.

That's why the message you'll find in these pages is a little different to what you might have read in other diet books, even the faith-based ones. You will not find any recipes here. There aren't any meal plans or exercise regimes. There will be no finger-wagging over your self-control or motivation, because this book was born from love.

I've been working as a nutritionist for over 20 years. I run a community called New Life Promise, which at the time of writing this book has over 33,000 members — a community of believers who have been exactly where you are right now. They all know the exact struggles you are facing — the anxiety, shame and frustration that happens when you just can't get your body to cooperate with you.

And all those beautiful souls have taught me something incredibly powerful: that healing and change do not come from a place of fear. Transformation — of your body, yes, but also of your heart and mind — can only come from a place of love. You cannot heal a body you hate, and that's why the focus here will be to heal and transform your emotional life, so that your body can eventually follow.

That might sound strange when you've heard for so long that you just need to eat less and move more... but after working with so many women just like you, I know that whether you lose the weight has very little to do with whether you have a green smoothie for breakfast or a stack of pancakes. No — it's about tending to your emotions, healing what has been hurt and broken, and allowing God's grace and love to show you how to care for your body in a new way.

Whether you have 50, 100 or 300 pounds to lose, I wrote this book to share with you the healing and freedom that comes when you can release this part of your journey to the Lord, and trust that He can use this experience for something good. This is a vulnerable place to be, which is why, when you're finished with this book, I hope you'll join us in the New Life Promise community. It is a space held together by faith and a shared understanding of how difficult this process of transformation can be.

All the women in this group know the pain and overwhelm that comes with not being able to live how you want to — not being able to enjoy your family, not being able to participate in things you love doing, not being able to relax around food. And they know it because they've been where you are: if you've been putting yourself aside for your entire life — to raise the kids, help with grandkids, to work and help support the family, to be active within the church — know that you're not alone. In many Christian communities, women internalize the message that it's their responsibility to take care of their husband, kids and community — no matter what it costs. But after years of putting everybody else first, you're left wondering how you got so unhealthy and so unhappy.

The only way to truly heal is to find peace and love in your body, just as it is right now. Self-acceptance of that kind might sound impossible to you, but you can't fast-forward over this part and expect change to stick. You have to find a way to love yourself as God loves you if you're going to start moving towards the hopes and dreams you have for yourself in the future. That might require unravelling a whole lifetime of external programming, negative self-talk, and destructive behaviors. But God will be there with you every step of the way, as will the beautiful New Life Promise community if you would like them to be.

Remember as we get started that there is more right with you than there is wrong, and that God has you in this place for a reason. He can do something good with it. Throughout this book you're going to hear from two women who have been just where you are — Jackie Jacobs and my sister, Vicky De Los Rios — who share their stories of how God has used their journeys for good and His glory. They remind us that, like He did with Job, God allows us to go through difficult things. But He always promises that He will be there with us. So it's up to us to accept that, to surrender to Him and say, "OK. I'm here. I trust You."

So even if you feel broken right now, listen to me: God can put all those pieces back together. My goal for this book is to help you see the truth in that statement, and to help you start to see yourself and your journey as He does. My prayer for you in this process is to transform the combative relationship you have with your body and your food — to have instead a peaceful and loving relationship with the vessel God gave you and the nourishment He provides us.

CHAPTER 1

About six months before I started working on this book, I got sick. Just before Christmas of 2020, I started having heartburn. It felt like a normal heartburn, like I'd had during my pregnancies, although I knew I wasn't pregnant. By Christmas Eve I was vomiting and couldn't keep anything down. Something was wrong, and the specialist I needed to see couldn't fit me in until the end of February. She put me on omeprazole to help control the reflux and sent me on my way. It took the heartburn down a notch, but I was eating so little that even just taking a shower would leave me dizzy. One day while home alone, I had a dizzy spell getting out of the shower and fell. I decided enough was enough, and found a functional medicine doctor and a naturopath who could help me until I could see the specialist.

But February was a long time away, and things went from bad to worse. Every time I tried to eat something, my stomach would be in agony. I lost so much weight that after I got down to below 90 pounds, I stopped getting on the scale — it made me feel so sick to see those numbers. I had no energy and could hardly get out of bed in the morning. And if I did make it out of bed, I hated getting dressed, because it looked like I was a little kid playing dress-up in her mom's clothes.

People stared at me when I left the house, and whispered to each other. I felt like they thought I'd done this to myself, like I'd done it on purpose.

Then one of the supplements I experimented with made my face break out so severely that I locked myself in my house for a month and did not leave even once. It was so painful. Putting make-up on it just made it worse, and it got so bad that it left scars all over my face and neck.

My body had revolted against me and I didn't know what to do.

Eventually we got it figured out. A few months earlier, I had taken a course of antibiotics for a tooth infection, and then another course soon after that when I got Covid-19. The two courses of antibiotics combined were effectively a toxic bomb to my small intestine and microbiome, and I had developed SIBO — small intestinal bacterial overgrowth.

The reason I'm telling you all this is simply to say: I understand what it is to suffer in your body, to hate your appearance and feel ashamed of what you've become. Yes, our experiences are different. I won't pretend to know what you've gone through in your journey to this point. But I do know how it feels to have your body refuse to cooperate with you. I do know the feeling of other people's judgments. I know how crushing it is to try everything you can think of... and still feel like a failure.

But the Lord knows the plans He has for us.

At the time of writing this book, I'm still on medication for SIBO and my skin is still healing. I've come to truly appreciate modern medicine! I can only eat a tiny handful of foods, my routine has changed completely, and at this stage, it remains to be seen what God is going to do with this situation. Maybe He will heal me and I'll get back to feeling like I did before, or maybe He won't — maybe He will use it to His glory in some other way.

And in case you think I seem very calm about that, let me tell you that I was *not* calm about it at all when it first started going down. I was a wreck. Not only did I feel betrayed by my body, I felt like I'd suffered a loss: the dreams and expectations I'd had about the future were no longer within my reach. After my face broke out, I thought, "What's next? Boils?!"

HELLO, JOB? I NEED SOME ADVICE.

We all know the story of Job. He's the Bible's poster child for sticking it out under suffering, right? So while I was deep in the midst of this illness, I thought, 'You know what? I'm going to see what Job did when he was really suffering.' I got my Bible and opened it up at Job 1:1.

"There once was a man named Job who lived in the land of Uz. He was blameless, a man of complete integrity."

'Well, shoot,' I thought. 'I can't even pretend to relate to that! I sure as heck ain't blameless, so I'm behind already!'

But I kept reading.

Because Job is such an upright man, Satan asks God if he can test him. God essentially says, "Test him, see what happens." Man, I get emotional thinking about this story, because Job stays faithful the whole time. Satan absolutely tortures him. Job is abandoned by everyone who should care for him. Even his wife starts to doubt. His friends ask him what he did to deserve all these terrible things — losing his kids, his crops failing, his health ruined. But he kept his faith, trusting in God through it all. Finally, when he cried out and asked the Lord why he was letting him suffer so much, God asked him who he was to question His plan. So Job stayed humble, and accepted that God had a plan, and soon enough everything he had lost was restored to him, and more.

God knows what He's doing with us. You might be wondering right now how you ended up where you are. You might have a lot of weight to lose, a family that's not supportive, and a whole lot of health issues to contend with. You might be wondering why you're suffering, if there's something you did that brought all this on you. Your story might end like Job's, or it may not. You may get to your goal weight, or you may not. What I learned from Job through all this was the only thing you can do is to trust in the Lord. Not to fight and strive and question, but to accept what is.

I'll tell you right now that I did not have the trust and faith that Job did when I searched out his story. In my misery, I was questioning God all the time. *Why would You let this happen to me? Why haven't You healed me yet? Why is nothing working?* But Job stayed strong, and when God saw that he had accepted His plan, He turned his life around. That inspired me to keep going. There's such peace in that level of acceptance. It's a rest from the constant effort of trying to get someplace else. You know the feeling — "Once I lose the weight, then I will wear a bathing suit and take my kids to the beach," or, "Once I lose the weight, I'll pick up that ministry again." And you will probably get there. My hope and my prayer is that you get there.

But what if you don't? Could that be OK? There's so much peace in accepting where you are today — not because you're not going to take action to change it, but in order to live in a state of love and joy as you do take action. In order to love your body while you heal it.

THERE'S MORE RIGHT WITH YOU THAN THERE IS WRONG

I want this book to help you see past your body and your suffering to what else is good in your life. It's easy to get very fixated on the problem, to the extent that it becomes your identity, and you lose sight of the blessings all around you. Maybe you have a great relationship with your spouse, you raised great kids, you're a beloved part of your community — there's a lot of great stuff about you that has nothing to do with your body.

God has given you a body as a great gift, but it's not the only thing about you that matters. Imagine that I came to your home and I brought you a gift — a little statue — and you put it up on a shelf. There are two ways you could react to this gift. The first is that you decide that you already had a lot of statues on your shelf, and it's really kind of annoying that I gave this to you, because now there is one more thing you have to take care of. And every time you look at it, you're annoyed at the fact that you have to take care of it.

But now let's say you put the statue on the shelf along with all your other things, and when you take care of it, you think of me and how much I must care about you to bring you a gift like that. So then you want to take care of it as an opportunity to connect with me, and so you actually enjoy taking care of it.

Most people are taking care of their body in the first scenario. They don't realize it, but what they're saying to

God is, "I'm annoyed that You gave this to me. I know you gave this to me as a gift, but I don't want to take care of it. It takes a lot of time and energy."

But what would it look like if it were the other way?

What if every day you could look at your body and think, "Thank you, heavenly Father, for this gift. Thank you for giving me this body. I'm looking forward to taking care of it today." How different would that be? Instead of constantly fixating on how you look and what other people are thinking, you could be focused on how incredible your body is. Because it *is* incredible — even if you don't feel good about it at the moment.

Your body isn't just its appearance — it's also doing a whole lot of stuff that God designed to keep you alive, so that you could live in His light. Right now, at this instant, your body is breathing, pumping blood, keeping your temperature at the right level, processing the words on this page, filtering toxins, releasing hormones and nutrients... it is busy in there! But when we're focused on our appearance alone, we can't appreciate all that. We can't see how much is going right, because we're only looking at what we think is wrong. But there's more right with you than there is wrong with you. I first heard that insight from an autoimmune specialist named Justin Janoska, and it has impacted me greatly, because it's such a refreshing perspective.

The chorus of one of my favorite Christian songs says: "If you're alive and breathing, praise the Lord." Some days, when my skin is at its worst or my stomach is really upset, I think, "Really? I need a little bit more than just being alive today to praise Him!" But the lyrics are right. There's always something about your body to be grateful for.

And in case you're struggling to think about what those might be, let me share some examples.

A friend of mine, Sean Stephenson, was born with a condition that put him in a wheelchair for his entire life. He was three feet tall and was never able to walk. He's passed now, but watching him living his life in praise of the Lord reminded me that simply being able to walk was something to be grateful for.

Through this SIBO journey, I've learned that there are people all over the world with an illness that doesn't allow them to eat any food at all. They can only have liquids, often through a drip. Discovering that made me realize that being able to eat anything at all is a blessing — being able to eat comfortably and to experience variety and flavor is something to be so grateful for.

I was able to have children in my thirties, with no complications — and what an incredible achievement *that* is for the body. If your body was able to bear children, praise God! Even if you weren't able to have children, if you have arms to hold your family members, a brain that recognizes your loved ones, and a body that allows you to be present with them, praise Him.

We can also look at the experiences of other people to recognize the things in ourselves that we don't value on a daily basis, as I learned from Sean. He couldn't walk. He had to have someone help him with just about everything he ever wanted to do. I don't. I don't have to have someone help me to function every day. I don't have to have someone drive me every time I want to go to the store or help me when I need to reach things in a cupboard. Even when my body feels limited, I'm still able to use it as I choose.

Take a moment here. What are a few things about your

body that you can be grateful for today? How could you enjoy taking care of your body in some way today?

Could you write those things on a note card and put it somewhere you're going to see it — like the bathroom or kitchen — to remind yourself of all the things about your body you can praise God for?

CHAPTER 2

God gave us an amazing imagination, didn't He? We can dream up limitless possibilities, in vivid color and surround sound. He gave us this vision so we could glorify Him… but most of the time, we use our imagination without consciously thinking about what we're doing. And because we're human, we end up dwelling on what we *think* other people are thinking about us. We assume the worst: that everyone is looking at all our flaws, wondering how on earth we could have let ourselves get this way.

But who is really judging you in that situation? Is it them? It might be, but unless someone comes out and says it to your face, you can't know. The only thing you know, in that imagined scenario, is that it came from your own brain, and so there's every chance that your own brain is where all that judgment is coming from too.

I came face to face with this one day when we were going to see some friends after about a year, just as my skin was starting to heal. I was looking in the mirror, imagining their reaction to the red, angry spots and all the scars. And then I started to ask myself questions, forcing myself to answer honestly.

Does it matter if the scars are uncovered?
Yes it does! It matters because we're gonna see our friends and I haven't seen them in a year and they're gonna judge me.
Will they not love you even with scars on your face?
Umm... Oh. They actually would probably still love me.
So who is the one that's judging?
I'm the one that's judging.
Why are you judging, Isabel?
Because this is not what I'm supposed to look like.
Says who?
I do.
Are you the final word on everything?
No, that's God's job.
And do you think God judges the scars on your face?
No. It's just me.

I took a deep breath and walked away from the mirror. Suddenly I felt OK. I was the only one who was judging me… and you may well be the only one judging you.

And if somebody else does judge you for how you look, that's about them. That's their responsibility — not yours. It's really none of your business what they think of you. But of course, there are situations where other people do take it upon themselves to let you know anyway. That's difficult and it can be extremely painful to hear.

In the New Life Promise group, the posts that break my heart the most are when one of our members shares that their spouse is being unkind or unsupportive. Maybe their husband tells them how fat they are every day, how lazy they are. How do you even begin to navigate that, when what you really need from that person is love and gentle support?

As far as I can see, there's only one thing for it. You have to make a choice, first thing in the morning, that God's opinion of you is the only one that matters. Before you even get out of bed in the morning, trust the day to Him, and ask Him to help you lift the shield of faith as many times as you need to throughout the day in order to protect yourself. So, when that person comes along and starts making those hurtful comments, you can deflect them. You can hold those comments up against what God would say about you, and decide which message you want to take into your heart.

(And here's a song recommendation to help you remember it throughout the day: "Who You Say I Am" by Hillsong Music.)

I want to choose what God says about me, every day. Maybe I didn't make the best choices up to this point, but He is a God of redemption, and I can make a different choice tomorrow. No matter what has happened today, yesterday, all the days before — He hasn't changed His mind about you, and you can be a new creation in Him every moment you choose.

When you find that level of peace in the morning, you keep it all day long. It feels like a sigh of relief, before anything has even happened. You can decide how you want to go about the day, how you want to interact with people. Having God's peace on your heart allows you to detach from the negative things in your imagination, and it allows you to put some distance between yourself and anything unkind that people say or do. Trust each day to Him, trust your heart to Him, let Him protect you when you're vulnerable.

Remember Exodus 14:14 — "The Lord will fight for you; you need only to be still."

ALLOW GOD TO FILL YOUR CUP

Some days, navigating the process of unravelling all the pain and emotional struggle around your weight is going to take it out of you. Whether you've been struggling with your weight for a couple of years or your whole life, you're most likely carrying around a whole lot of emotional and mental baggage about what your weight means about you. And there's a good chance that the thoughts and stories you have about this topic have become habitual — you dwell on them often, ingraining them deeper and deeper into your brain and spirit.

Resolving and releasing those thoughts and stories is the crucial step in finding your freedom. They are an additional burden you just don't need to carry, and the work of actually physically losing the weight is going to be much, much easier if you're not lugging all that emotional pain around with you too.

That's why, over the next couple of chapters, we're not going to talk about your weight very much at all, and that's because you don't need to hear any more about it. You already know about the health benefits of changing your diet and exercise. You've already tried to change, maybe many times before! You have a dozen reasons *why* you want to change. But actually making those changes stick? Well, that's much more complicated than whether you eat more candy than carrots. Making the changes stick is all about dealing with the underlying emotional experiences that shape your behavior and beliefs. We need to start to untangle the emotional, psychological and spiritual knots that have tied you up before you'll be able to make the lasting physical changes you really want to see.

At this point I want to share Jackie Jacobs' story. Jackie is from a small town in Tennessee, and joined New Life Promise several years ago. She had finally decided it was time to trust her weight loss journey to the Lord when she realized that she no longer knew how much she weighed — her scale stopped measuring at 500 pounds and she had passed that. Here's Jackie on how she got to that point — and how she got back down to 170.

~

"Gaining weight like I did doesn't happen overnight. It's a lifetime of choosing bad foods, and choosing food to be my comfort instead of God. It started in my early childhood, when I was 2. My mother, father, sister and I were in a car accident, and my mother was killed that day by a drunk driver. She leaned over to protect me, and she died from her injuries. My father worked and my mother had always taken care of us, so now we were in a new situation. He remarried shortly after my mom died, and his new wife was very young, just 18. I think she was unsure about how to take care of us — she hadn't really ever been around children that much — and she dug out a box that had my bottles in it. She filled those bottles back up with milk and that comforted me. I think that even at that very young age, I learned to seek comfort in food.

Broken children become broken adults, and I carried all that trauma into my marriage. It was a difficult marriage and a horrible divorce. There must be such a thing as a normal marriage, but I can promise you that mine was about the furthest thing from it — and I turned to food all the way through it. One horrible night soon before our divorce, I confronted my ex-husband about what was going on and he had a nervous breakdown and attacked me. He brought his own brokenness to the table — I realize now that he was dealing with his own struggles and I was just on the receiving end of them. But at the time it was like living in a prison. I had recurring nightmares about that night — that he was choking me, screaming that someone like me didn't deserve to be alive, when someone as good as my mother was dead. Even once the divorce was done, I'd wake up so upset and terrified that I couldn't go back to sleep. So I'd go to the pantry, and over the next two years, the 350-pound person I was became a 500-pound person. Eating was the only thing that made me feel OK.

I never told anybody what happened, but we lived in a small town. People talked. People laughed at my son and I while we were in line at the grocery store. It was entertainment to them, but it was our pain. They didn't really understand what we were going through, and we just had to deal with it. And the only way I could deal with it was to eat even more.

I'd been walking with God for about a year before I really got clear that I needed to lose the weight. But I didn't ask God to help me with my weight at first. He had helped me find forgiveness on so many levels, He had helped me do so many other things, so why didn't I ask Him at first? I really don't know. I think I was ashamed and embarrassed, because it was a sin I had done to myself. I didn't feel right asking Him to help me. So I did the same thing I had done over and over and over again. I went gung-ho into a yo-yo diet. I was going to lose the weight and I was going to keep it off!

I would do great for a couple of months, lose some weight, then a stressful time would come and I would go back to my old habits. Not only would I gain back everything I'd lost, but 10 more pounds with it. Even walking with God, I couldn't escape it. I had been doing well for a while, but then my dad's health declined, and some more stuff about my ex-husband came out. I had lost about 60 pounds at that point, and I put 40 of it back on right away. It happens before you even realize it, because you don't get on the scales when you know you're not doing good. You only get on the scales when you're trying!

A few years ago I reconnected with a lot of my college friends and we had a 4th of July party. We had a ball together. I had just had wrist surgery, so when I got home I was unloading the car, trying to carry everything without putting pressure on my wrist. I thought I was still a step away from the sidewalk, but I wasn't. So I stumbled and fell over. It didn't hurt me, I just laughed at myself at first and tried to get up. But I couldn't. I was still in a good mood, still laughing at myself — I was thinking of that old commercial about a lady who fell and couldn't get up, and it was funny because now I was that lady! But after about 30 minutes of trying to get up, it wasn't so funny anymore. I really could not get up. I was stuck on the ground and I could not do a thing about it.

So I prayed. "God, please help me get up. Please just help me." But He let me stay there. In the end I had to call some of my son's friends to come over and help me. It was humiliating. I was so embarrassed. My weight had gotten so out of control that I couldn't even get up off the sidewalk. And that night, God and I had a long talk. I said, "OK, God. You've helped me find forgiveness. You've helped me learn to love myself a little bit. Now help me with this. Will you help me with my weight?" And He said, "I've always wanted to help you with it Jackie. You just never asked. This is your struggle, and I want to help you with all your struggles."

Well let me tell you: it was *on* from that moment. I have had the most incredible story of healing, and it's a story that only God could write. I couldn't have done this on my own. There were so many days I felt like I was walking two steps behind Him, but every time, He would look back and say, "It's OK, Jackie — just keep your eyes focused on Me. You can't do it alone, but you can do it with Me."

Doctors told me that at my age, my chance of losing the weight without surgery was about 0.05%. I knew I couldn't do it alone. But with God I could. I did not have weight loss surgery. I never wanted to go that route —I put the weight on by myself, and God told me I could take it off. I didn't want a surgery that was going to cut off 90% of my stomach to be the answer. I wanted to do it the right way — one pound at a time, one day at a time, with God as my strength.

So that's how it happened: one pound at a time, one day at a time. It was a daily choice I had to make. Nobody was going to do the work for me — not even God. A lot of times He had to tap me on the shoulder and say, "Here's your shovel! I think you left it back there. Time to get back to work?" He wasn't going to do it for me, but He was going to walk beside me and be my strength. But I had to do the work. Was it hard? You betcha. Hardest thing I've ever done. Every other attempt I had made in my own strength lasted for about 60 days, and then it would all come crashing down. But in His strength, it's lasted for over five years.

Without God, I was trying to do it on my own strength, so I would lean more towards the boxed foods, things out of the freezer section and so on. They were low calorie, but I didn't know about all the processed ingredients in them that can also have an effect on the body. But when I did it with God, relying on His strength to guide my decisions, I was able to do it in a healthier way, with more fresh foods. And I feel so much better. When God's in the mix, everything is better. Everything is easier. And on the days when I had no strength at all, He was my strength... and I had a lot of those days. You can't lose 330 pounds and not have a whole lot of days that you have to turn to Him!

It was a struggle, because when I'd lost 100 pounds, I still had over 200 to go. But that's when my faith really kicked in. That's what drew me closer to God. I couldn't see a way to do it, but God said again, "I am the way, Jackie. I've always been the way, and you can do it with Me." And together we did it all.

I used to live to eat. Today I eat to live. I still have to choose every day whether I'm going to eat healthy or if I'm going to eat that junk food, and I'm the only person that can make that choice. But I love eating my healthy food now. I don't crave junk any more like I used to. Back when I started, I could have eaten a cardboard box some days, and I'm not lying to you! The cravings were very real and they were a struggle. I knew that with God I could do it, but it doesn't go away overnight. It's not going to happen fast. It's a journey of healing, and we've gotta be patient. There were many weeks that I didn't lose anything, the scale stayed exactly the same. One time I was pushing myself hard in the pool, and I didn't lose anything for two weeks! I got so mad that I walked outside and threw my scales in the trash. And that was the best thing I ever did! Because if I'm eating right, if I'm living right, the number on the scale is going to come down. You've just gotta have patience and believe in the process.

Today, I am truly happy for the first time in my adult life. I enjoy life, to the fullest. I get to work in outreach ministries that I feel God calling me to. I'm looking forward to my son getting married this year and being able to buy a dress at a regular store that fits. My daily struggle as that 500-pound person was that it took all the strength I had just to get out of bed. My back killed me, my knees killed me, I was miserable on the inside and out. I hated the person I'd become. I felt hopeless. But today I live in the freedom of Christ. I enjoy every day. I can get around without any problems. I can walk for miles, I can swim — I can do so much, and I can finally be the person Christ calls me to be. I'm free from the prison of that 500-pound body, and free from the food."

~

I love Jackie's story. It's so powerful — she worked incredibly hard, but in the end it was God's strength that carried her through.

Out in the world we often hear things like, "Put your own mask on first before helping others." But when you live as a believer, you know that your purpose here on this earth is to be Christ to other people. And so the only way that you are going to have the strength to take care of your own needs *and* to help other people too, is if you allow God to help you. Let Him be the one to put the mask on you. Let Him be the one to fill your cup, to give you the energy and strength to take care of yourself and the people who are depending on you.

Because sometimes you are just not going to be able to put your own mask on. Sometimes you just have to allow God to step in and carry you when you're in a situation you just can't manage. I remember one time that my mom was in hospital for three weeks with pneumonia on a ventilator. My dad was obviously in a difficult place emotionally, and I wanted to support him... but of course I myself was also in a difficult place. The hospital was an hour away, so I was traveling every single day, back and forth to the hospital. And I just couldn't do everything I needed to in order to "put my own mask on." I couldn't exercise every day, I couldn't get enough sleep, I couldn't make the healthiest possible meals. I just had to wake up in the morning, put some food in a cooler, get myself to the hospital and do what I needed to for my mom.

It was a powerful lesson that I just really needed to allow the Lord to step in. I asked Him to keep His healing hand on my body during that time, and to help me, give me discernment about what I could take on and what would have to wait.

It's uncomfortable, there's no doubt about that. It doesn't feel like we're doing enough — we all want to jump into every situation headfirst and push ourselves as hard as we can, but it doesn't work. Trying to handle everything in our own strength doesn't work. But if we can trust in the Lord, if we can learn to rely on Him in those times, that's how our relationship with Christ grows. Allowing Him to fill your cup is the only way you're going to be able to do all the things you need to do on this journey. It's the only way you'll be able to cook the healthy meals, get outside for a walk, get to bed on time… and still be there as you want to be for your family and community and work.

And ultimately what we need on a journey like this is discernment. We need to ask the Lord to help us see what we need to do ourselves, where we can ask for help, and what we can put aside for the moment. And God will do that for you. He will fill your cup and be your strength if you can let Him. And when you start to trust Him, He's going to give you the discernment that today is the day to ask your kids or husband for help making dinner. He's going to show you when it's time to let other people look after you. He's going to tell you when it's time to strive, and when it's time to get on the couch with your favorite blankie and just rest.

That discernment comes as your relationship with Him grows. And that relationship grows in the same way any relationship does — by spending time and actively paying attention to what you're hearing, actively tending to your connection. As you nurture that relationship, spending quiet time with Him in prayer, shutting off the world, and really listening to what He has to say, then the voice of the Holy Spirit just gets louder and stronger, and that's where that powerful discernment comes from.

Life in the world today is so busy. It's so loud. We're always on our phones, looking at TV and the internet, checking social media, constantly thinking about what's next, never taking any time just to be still — and we wonder why we don't hear from God. I think it's because we're hearing so much other stuff that His voice gets drowned out. He's always there, always ready to speak to us, but He's not going to force us to listen, and so we have to make that time to stop and listen to what God and the Holy Spirit are saying.

I've learned this as I've made more and more time to

spend with Him — instead of just a few moments here and there. Not just reading my devotional book for five minutes and then saying a quick prayer so I can get on with my day. No — real time. If the extent of your connection with someone is just saying a quick hello each morning, there's really no relationship there. But if you sit down and have a real conversation every day? Then that relationship is going to start to thrive, and the discernment and strength that we need from Him is going to start to come through.

That all sounds easy enough, right? But if you're anything like me and most of the women in the New Life Promise community, you've built your life around *doing* things, accomplishing things, serving people and keeping your family and community moving. I'm proud of what I've been able to accomplish in my life. You have many things to be proud of too. But the Lord says in Psalm 46:10, "Be still, and know that I am God."

Be still. He wants us to rest, and to trust Him to be God, trust Him to lead us, trust Him to be our strength. And I'm starting to think He might have a point, because everything I've accomplished in my own strength has taken a toll on me. Everything the women in New Life Promise have accomplished in their own strength has taken a toll on them. By thinking that we can do it all, we've all exhausted our bodies to the point that they start breaking down on us. I know you can relate: you work so hard to honor what He asks of us, to be the wife, mother and believer He wants us to be… but doing that in your own strength robs your body of its health and leaves you feeling like a failure.

As you heard from Jackie, handing over control to the Lord is a liberating, powerful choice. Allowing Him to be your strength changes everything. When you allow Him to fill your cup, it overflows. When my SIBO hit me hardest, I had to hand over control to Him, and He was there. My husband stepped in to help more with the kids' schooling. My kids started taking more responsibility for themselves. My dad was able to help out looking after the house. But the biggest place I saw God step in — in the most amazing way — was in New Life Promise, in our business. I have never worked so little as I did during the months that I was sick. It wasn't that I suddenly became lazy, but I had good days and bad days, and on the bad days, I wasn't able to do very much at all. And through what could only be the grace of God, this business has grown exponentially in a way that I can't take the credit for. I can truly only give Him the glory, because I was busy sitting on the couch, under a blankie, with a heating pad on my stomach, and He was busy moving mountains to get the right people in place to do everything that needed to happen.

I have phenomenal employees. We've set the business up to function well. But things just took off in a way that I can only explain as His hand moving according to His purpose. Every time I wanted to take back control, start striving again, I would notice that verse from Psalms, hanging above our fireplace: *Be still, and know that I am God.* I don't think it's an accident that we hung that verse there years ago. I needed to see it every single day during this journey — and maybe you will too.

So if you feel like your body has broken down on you, if you are despairing over how you look and feel, here's my encouragement to you: God is ready and willing to step in and take care of things. Know that in the most amazing way, He has a plan to use your situation for good. Even if it seems like He's saying no to your prayers right now, sometimes it's so that He can say yes to something so much bigger. Can you trust Him to put His healing hand on your life, to do something great with you... and to follow where He asks you to go, even if you can't see the way through right now? If the Holy Spirit is calling you to rest right now, instead of striving to change yourself, can you listen? If He's calling you to stop and heal spiritually before you heal physically, can you let Him help you in that process?

CHAPTER 3

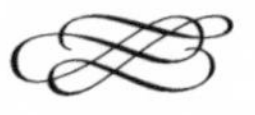

LEARNING TO REST

In Matthew 11:28, Jesus says, "Come to me, all you who are weary and burdened, and I will give you rest."

Does that sound like you? Weary? Burdened? Jesus is inviting you to rest, to put your heavy burdens down and allow Him to restore you. Could you lay the burden of your weight, and everything that happened to get you to this point, at His feet?

Rest is so powerful. Rest is how healing happens. But we are terrified of rest, because our culture equates rest with laziness.

I am here to tell you that they are not the same thing. God is very clear about the importance of rest: it's why He created the Sabbath. He knows that people — no matter their walk of life or what their responsibilities are — need to rest. It's non-negotiable with Him. In His eyes, rest is just as important as work: you are refreshing your strength and spirit in order to continue doing His work and living a good life.

Now, rest doesn't have to mean sitting on the couch doing nothing all day. Rest can be fun! But as women we often work so much that we forget how to have fun. If it means watching a funny Netflix series that takes me out of my life for a little bit, that's fun. If it's just playing Monopoly with my kids, which they really like and makes me be more present — that's fun too. Reading books with my kids is restful for me. Taking a long walk out in nature on a beautiful day is restful. Anything that takes me out of my head and makes me forget about my to-do list counts.

Sometimes I just sit out on our back patio and look around, watching the garden and listening to nature. If that's not great, I don't know what is. Yes, I could be washing dishes, or hanging laundry, or preparing dinner. But just sitting there feels so restorative, and it gives me the energy I need to go and do all those things later — with a better attitude and a spring in my step.

One of my employees always says, "Don't 'should' on me." I laughed so much when I first heard her say that, but there's a lot of truth to it: many of us have people in our lives who think we should be doing all kinds of things. We *should* eat healthier. We *should* exercise more. We *should* do more ministry at church. We *should* be more available for them. But that's not for other people to decide. What you *should* be doing is between you and God. And I suspect that if you are weary and burdened, He might think you *should* take some time to rest and restore yourself.

Of course, the person who says we *should* do anything the loudest is always our own self. Grace has already been given to us without restriction... but we're terrible at extending that grace to ourselves. I *should* eat that salad. I *should* go for that walk. I *shouldn't* have had that cookie. I *shouldn't* have stayed in bed this morning. It's exhausting, isn't it? Listen to what you say to yourself, to the words and judgements that run through your mind all day. Would you talk to somebody else like that? Of course not — that would be cruel and unfair. God calls us to love one another, and that includes yourself. If you wouldn't say those things to a loved one, then surely it's not loving to say them to yourself.

A big part of our problem with rest comes down to the fact that the expectations on women (and men too) in the world today are completely unrealistic. Not only do we have to take care of our homes, raise our children, cook multiple meals a day and support our community, but we have to work, commute, take care of ageing parents and help out at church too. Some of the pressure comes from society, and some of it comes from ourselves. But there's no denying that we have got far too much on our plates, and if we're going to have any chance of handling all of it, we're going to need to ask for help, first and foremost from God, for His strength, but from the people around us too.

I ask God on a daily basis to show me what other people can do to help me. I'm not saying "Lord, please come down from the heavens and do my laundry," but I have said, "Lord, how on earth am I going to do all this laundry?!" And I have heard so clearly, "Your kids are old enough to wash their own clothes." Other days, He has said, "There are five able bodies that live in your house, not just one." So now my first prayer every day is to remember that, and to look for opportunities to allow other people to take responsibility, to grow and to support me.

When my kids were young, I got overwhelmed trying to handle being involved in many different ministries in the church all at once. I couldn't figure out how my neighbor was doing so much in the church and I barely had time to breathe. I was constantly comparing myself to everything she was doing. One day she said to me, "Isabel, my kids are older, so you can't compare what I'm doing to what you're doing. We're in different seasons of our lives." She taught me to ask for that guidance from God, to ask what He would have me do — not what I would have me do, not what the world would have me do, but what He would have me do.

Remember, in this season of your life — where maybe it's time to focus on your health and your own priorities for a while — that even Jesus didn't do His work alone. He had His disciples to help Him, His family — He found some wonderful, imperfect people to help Him do everything He needed to get done. He knew they wouldn't get everything right all the time, and still He trusted them to be His hands and feet. So sure — maybe my 12 year-old isn't going to do the laundry exactly as I would do it. Maybe your husband isn't going to cook dinner exactly as you would do it. Maybe your colleague isn't going to do the presentation the same way you would do it. But is that OK, if it all gets done and nothing is ruined, and it takes the pressure off you for a time? Jesus thought so.

BEING VULNERABLE

I had never realized the importance of fellowship, especially communing with other women, like I did during the period when my skin was so badly broken out that I couldn't bear to see anyone. I hid at home and wouldn't go out, because I didn't want anyone to look at me. It was so painful and lonely that eventually my mother-in-law came to knock some sense into me. She refused to let me stay by myself for such long stretches any more. She didn't try to find the right words, she didn't try to make me feel better — she just sat with me in our rocking chairs on the porch while I cried and talked and cried and talked. She didn't try to fix anything, but she acknowledged that the situation was hard, and that I was suffering. I couldn't have guessed how much better that would make me feel. I always felt like a different person after spending a few hours with her, and just allowing myself to be truly honest and real about how much I was struggling.

The more we shove our emotions down into our bodies where we don't have to deal with them, the more painful they eventually become. The only way the pain goes away is if you let it out —acknowledge it, speak the truth of it. Jesus said that the truth will set us free — and the truth is most powerful when it's spoken out loud. I'm not saying you have to tell everyone you meet about your deepest darkest emotions — it's important to distinguish between who is a safe person to share this with and who is not — but once you know who your safe people are, it's so powerful to start talking it out. Or crying it out. I spent a whole lot of time crying, because I regretted how badly I had treated my body over the years, which had made it susceptible to this kind of damage. But having someone kind and courageous witness that pain, hold it for you so that you can breathe for a moment — that's so precious. Find those friends, those family members, even a therapist if that feels safer, and trust them to walk beside you as you start this process of healing.

A funny thing happens when you let people in like this. Instead of pushing them away, or making them uncomfortable, it strengthens your relationship. Letting people see you in a new light, in a vulnerable light, as God sees you — it deepens your love and understanding of one another. Let it all come out. Let them see all your fear and anger and shame. They might surprise you.

One day I was talking to my friend Michelle, wishing desperately that my work didn't need me to spend most of my time on camera, showing my face to people. Michelle laughed and said, "No one likes perfect people! What if you just show up imperfectly?" *Ooooh. Yikes.* It made me really uncomfortable to consider showing up in videos with my face all red and scarred, but she was right. Not only did it draw me closer to the women in my community — who also don't want to let people see them — but it gave me a hint of how God might be using my experience to bring healing to others too.

Vulnerability is hard. But it's transformative, and that transformation happens when you walk in faith with the people who love you, letting them support you and pray for you. That's why James 5:16 says, "Confess your sins to each other and pray for each other so that you may be healed. The prayer of a righteous person is powerful and effective."

CHAPTER 4

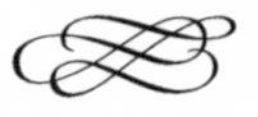

When I started New Life Promise, we began a private Facebook group, like many programs do. And I was told by some other coaches and nutritionists that sometimes their members use it, sometimes they don't. But the New Life Promise group is incredibly active. At the time of writing this book, there are over 33,000 people in there, and when someone posts something, it's very common for them to get 100 or 200 comments on their posts. There are some posts that have over 500 comments on them.

And while we do get nutrition questions occasionally, most of the posts are from people who are desperate for help and support. "Please pray for me — this is the tenth diet that I've been on and I'm so scared that I'm going to fail once again." Then the next one will be, "Will you pray for me? I'm trying so hard to follow this program, but it feels like my husband and children are sabotaging me." Then another will say, "Could you pray for me please? I'm feeling so much guilt about the state my body is in that some days I just want to quit."

The vast majority of what people share in the community are about the emotions they are experiencing. And the more people share, the more courage it gives other people to share. It has become a beautiful place — a completely safe and vulnerable space for people to talk about their struggles and receive the love and support they so deeply need. It's been a huge privilege for me to see the community become so strong together, and it has taught me something so powerful: that food isn't the hard part of weight loss.

Yes, it can be challenging to break old habits and overcome cravings. But the hard part is navigating all the emotions that make you turn to food in the first place. The reason people are "failing" on a diet or not feeling able to navigate their health is far more about what's going on in their life, rather than not knowing that a home-cooked meal would be better for them than a TV dinner. I think if I gave most people a nutrition test, they would at least score a B or B+. Most people know what's good for them and what's not when it comes to their food. But the reason people don't make those healthy choices — even when they know what they are? That's what we're here to figure out, and that's what the amazing people in the New Life Promise community have helped me understand.

For many years, I taught nutrition from a place of fear.

I became a nutritionist because my mom was very overweight and very sick all throughout my childhood, and it caused her so much suffering. When I was in my teens, she was diagnosed with Type 2 diabetes, and then things really started to spiral. Soon she was on diabetes medication, and then medication for high cholesterol, and then medication for high blood pressure. And one of those medications, or the combination of them, started to damage her kidneys. She ended up on dialysis for four years, and eventually she had to have a kidney transplant.

Watching my mom struggle with her weight and all the illnesses it caused her taught me to live in a state of fear that any day now, my body was going to break down on me. I was terrified that I would end up like her. I was so scared that I would get sick, that my husband would get sick, that my kids would get sick, and I taught nutrition to other people from that same place of fear, to stop them from getting sick. Sure, I was teaching people how to eat nutritious food that would help them be healthy, but it always came with the warning to eat this way "so you don't get diabetes or have a heart attack."

But there's so much more to nutrition and health than not getting sick. There's so much vitality, energy and opportunity that comes from learning to love and trust your body, and eventually I realized that my fear had been stopping me from trusting in God to use every situation to His own glory. Through the New Life Promise community, and this experience I've had with SIBO, He showed me that I'm called to spend my time helping people heal from a place of love — not to spend my time fretting about things that might not happen.

What I've learned over the years is that if you don't allow yourself to feel these emotions, like fear, they get trapped in your body. You hold on to them, often without even realizing it, until they form a kind of prison around you. These emotions have likely been part of your experience for years, maybe even decades, or a whole lifetime. And most people want to skip the step of dealing with that history and go straight to giving up sugar and going to the gym four times a week. I get it! Feeling your feelings sucks! It's hard, and I *wish* the other way worked... but it's this emotional part that trips you up. Yo-yo dieting? That's emotional dieting. God made our bodies to be extremely intelligent — and when we try to skip ahead in the process, before we're ready, our body will send us straight back to the start to slow down and do it properly.

So instead of making any changes to your diet or lifestyle right now, I invite you simply to do the work in this book — the emotional, spiritual work of squaring with yourself and God, taking a clear look at your past and what happened to get you here. We want any changes you make to come from a loving place — not a fearful, angry or hateful place. Change only sticks when you can truly accept yourself right here, where you're starting from. If that means you need to do this emotional work before you give up the chocolate, that's fine. There are a lot of people in New Life Promise who gave up the chocolate first and then had to go back and do the emotional work later, but let me tell you — putting down the chocolate is much easier when you know why you're picking it up in the first place.

FEELING YOUR FEELINGS

I want you to prepare yourself to deal with some emotions, maybe for the first time, that you have been forcing down into your body, and holding on to for many years. It's not your fault that you haven't let yourself process these feelings until now — maybe you've never had a safe place to explore them, or even just an opportunity to spend some time putting your own wellbeing first. But now I'm inviting you not just to deal with the feelings, but to pray about them and make this healing process part of your relationship with God in a way you might not have felt was possible before.

I invite you to consider that maybe these emotions are the reason that your health is where it is right now and why your weight has gotten to where it is today. Consider that maybe the reason you feel the way you do about yourself is that these emotions have piled up in your body without you even noticing, and they've festered there, tainting how you see yourself and blocking you from moving forward. Or maybe these feelings are right up in your face — maybe they're unavoidable and you're thinking, "Isabel, these dang emotions are all I feel every day!" Either way — it's OK. This is a safe place to start to untangle all the emotional complexity that has sprung up around your health, so that you can release what's no longer serving you and start to follow the Lord into the beautiful future He has for you.

When I announced in the New Life Promise Facebook group that I was going to write this book, I asked the community to share the emotions that they've experienced since starting on their journey towards healing. There are a lot of them! Some of these might pertain to you, or all of them might. I encourage you to read through each one and consider your own experiences:

- Have I felt this emotion, or do I feel it currently?
- Have I buried this emotion down in my body because it's too difficult to deal with?
- Could I pray about this emotion today?
- What does the Holy Spirit start to tell me about how this feeling affects me when I really start to listen to Him?

Take your time going through this section. I've split each emotion into its own section, because there's a lot to work through, and it can be tough to realize just how much pain and judgement have become trapped within your body. You might have memories that need to be relived and then released to the Lord, or nasty comments from other people that you buried deep down might suddenly come up and force you to deal with them. All of it is OK. There's no time pressure here, there's nothing for you to tick off a to-do list — just sit quietly with God and allow Him to lead you through it all.

And if you feel overwhelmed or the Lord hasn't yet lifted a burden from you, remember that it's perfectly fine to seek out people who will support you along the way. The New Life Promise community is one such place, the safe people you've chosen from your life are another, and I think it's always beneficial to find a therapist who understands what you're going through and can support you from a gentle, neutral position. I worked with a therapist all through my illness and the Lord used her in a powerful way to facilitate my healing.

Before we start in on all the different emotions, I'd like you to take a moment to pray. Get still, find that place in your heart where you feel God's love, and ask Him to come and be with you as you set out on this journey of healing your body and soul. Ask the Holy Spirit to help you surrender this process to His strength, His grace, and for the courage to trust Him every step of the way. Pray, too, for contentment. Ask the Lord to help you love yourself where you are right now, so that you can start feeling joy again, *today*. Ask Him to help you forgive your body, and to bring peace to your spirit that will stay with you, no matter how long it takes to fully heal.

FEAR

Fear happens when we stir up reactions in our bodies about things that haven't happened yet. We are projecting and predicting that we'll get a particular outcome, but often there is really no evidence that this is going to be the result. You might feel afraid that your health and weight are going to continue to become more difficult to manage... but there's the same probability of it getting worse as it getting better. So why not focus on getting better? All of our fears are either based on things that have happened in the past or things that have happened to other people — and those things are not necessarily going to be true for you.

One of the biggest fears people are experiencing in our community is the fear of failure. They don't want to try to lose weight again, because they're so afraid of 'failing' again. This fear of failure is rooted in the value we put on what other people think. Sure, we don't want to disappoint ourselves, but we're more afraid of looking like a failure in front of other people. And the fear of failure is really paralyzing for a lot of people. Maybe you can relate — the fear becomes so strong that you would rather just stay where you are now, rather than even take the risk of trying something new. Where you are right now might be miserable, but at least it's familiar! We are so uncomfortable with the unknown, and the unknown is what's on the other side of trying a new meal plan for a few weeks.

If we can just detach from what the world thinks, or from what a certain person thinks, and focus instead on what our heavenly Father thinks, and what we think of ourselves, then we can start to release our fear, bit by bit. Fear takes up a lot of room in our brain, and doesn't always leave much space for thinking about anything else, so as we learn to detach from our fears, we can start to ask more interesting questions: what if every failure wasn't actually a failure, but a lesson?

There are so many different diets, nutrition protocols, exercise programs and supplements to try. You might think that you failed on the Keto Diet, for example, or on the Paleo Diet. But you didn't fail. It probably just wasn't the right diet for you — maybe you need something less restrictive. You might think that you failed with Weight Watchers, or the calorie-counting plan a nutritionist gave you. But you didn't fail with those either — maybe spending so much time measuring and tracking tiny details doesn't work for your personality or lifestyle. Each attempt is a success in its own way, in that it showed you what *you* specifically need or don't need. Not what your neighbor needs, not what your sister needs, but what *you* need. It's no failure to start ruling things out — each experiment is simply moving you closer to the right approach.

'Just detaching' from fear, though, is a lot easier said than done.

The only way I know to get over it is doing the 'What If' exercise. Let's say your fear of failure would make you think, "I'm afraid I'm going to fail on this diet." Well, OK. What if you do? Would God still love you? Would you still be part of a community? Could you try again? Could you find a community or nutrition partner to support you during the moments you struggle? Could you trust the Lord to do something good with you, even if you don't stick to this or that diet?

God is above your diet. He's bigger than any 'failure' of ours. Accepting that, trusting this learning curve to Him

— that's how you find peace and relief from this fear of failure.

A lot of people are also terrified that their efforts won't work — that they'll try a new plan and not lose any weight. In that situation, you feel like you're setting yourself up for disappointment. But even that is a lesson — if you followed a meal plan for a month and you didn't lose any weight, you learned something about yourself in that time. Maybe you shouldn't eat something in that meal plan. Maybe you need more food than the plan suggests. Maybe you need less. Once you can change your relationship with failure, so that you can see each experience as a lesson instead, you're free to experiment more and stay more optimistic about the future.

Now, some people are going to be undoing a lifetime of feeling like a failure, and of fearing failure. This change won't happen overnight. But life is a lot more peaceful when you can create that perspective.

It's not just fear of failure, though. Fear is one of the deepest and most powerful emotions that human beings experience. We learn fear in childhood, and often the things that scared us back then still have an effect on us today. I was talking to my therapist just recently about how much fear I still experience as an adult, and she asked me: "Where did you learn that you have to live your life in fear?"

We pick up fears all throughout our life, but when it comes to our bodies and appearances, our fears can become very deeply intertwined with our need to belong and to be loved. When we feel like we're not physically 'enough', we can start to fear all kinds of pain and rejection. We start to worry that our loved ones will pull away from us, or that we'll be physically unable to stay connected with them, either because we're too big, too sick, or that we'll be gone too soon.

But letting yourself get caught up in anxiety and a fear of the future just forces you to suffer the potential outcome twice: you go through all the anguish and suffering just from imagining it — which leaves you with less energy and emotional resilience to deal with it if the event actually does happen! And of course, it might not happen, and then you've made yourself suffer unnecessarily.

In the book *Respectable Sins,* Jerry Bridges highlights the sins that we've started to tolerate and accept as a society, and one of them was anxiety and worry. He points out that anxiety and worry are essentially a lack of trust in God, and boy did that hit me hard! When I first got sick, all my symptoms suggested that I could have Crohn's disease, and for days I was in total freefall: *what am I going to do? What if I have Crohn's? I don't want to live like that!* But then I realized that if I kept catastrophizing about it, before I had any diagnosis, I was essentially saying to God, "I don't think you have everything under control, so I'm going to keep putting my energy towards it." It stopped me from spiralling in my worst moments, because I believe that He does have it under control, and always has. Now, that's not to say that He's just going to go ahead and fix everything. My body is not working the right way, and it may never. But what I do know, and I know this for sure, is that He is going to take this situation and make something good of it.

Dr. Brené Brown says that shame is about who you are, while guilt is about something you did. In her words, guilt says, "I'm sorry — I made a mistake," while shame says, "I'm sorry — I *am* a mistake."

Shame is the embarrassment you feel about who you are at this very moment. Shame is the reason you're having a hard time accepting yourself as you are, because somewhere along the way, you internalized that there's something fundamentally wrong with you.

For some people, this is the result of abuse earlier in their life, which creates a huge amount of shame, and often leads to overeating as a way to protect yourself from attention and the possibility of further trauma. If that's your experience, it's important to seek out help from a therapist or mental health professional who can support you through recovery. But for many people, shame simply comes from the cruel or careless comments other people make, the undisguised looks in our direction, or our own expectations about how we're supposed to be.

No matter its source, shame is compounded by your imagination of what other people must think of you. Maybe you believe that other people are thinking, "She must just eat all kinds of stuff. She's lazy. She doesn't take care of herself. She has no self-control." But what those people can't see are all the facts: a challenging childhood or being a single parent, for example, or the simple fact that your health got away from you because you put so much effort into taking care of everyone else.

In her book *Daring Greatly,* Dr. Brown says:

> "Shame derives its power from being unspeakable... When we experience shame, we feel disconnected and desperate for worthiness. When we're hurting, either full of shame or even just feeling the fear of shame, we are more likely to engage in self-destructive behaviors...
>
> If we can share our story with someone who responds with empathy and understanding, shame can't survive. Self-compassion is also critically important, but because shame is a social concept — it happens between people — it also heals best between people. A social wound needs a social balm, and empathy is that balm. Self-compassion is key because when we're able to be gentle with ourselves in the midst of shame, we're more likely to reach out, connect, and experience empathy."

Shame cannot withstand having a light shone upon it. It cannot withstand vulnerability.

Like Dr. Brown says, shame is a social wound — it typically starts with the people who are closest to us, often the people who live in the very same house. It's very difficult when those people add shame to your load. Not only is it painful, but it's clear that those people are not safe to be vulnerable with. You might have to put up your shield of faith, and consciously decide that you're not going to accept those comments anymore. When you come home with your healthy food and your husband rolls his eyes and says, "Oh no, not this again!" you're going to have to ask God for the strength to say to yourself, "No, I don't have to take on that perspective. I know what I need to do for myself." And then you can turn to your safe people, and get the support you need there.

The only way to get past shame is to offer ourselves grace, to allow ourselves to be vulnerable with people who can support us, and to realize that God can do something with where we are right now, no matter where we're coming from.

GUILT

Guilt happens when you've internalized a story about your situation: that you've done this to yourself, and so now you feel like you deserve your suffering because of your past actions.

A lot of women in the New Life Promise community have a lot of guilt that because of their weight, they're not being the kind of wife, mother or friend they want to be. But where is that guilt coming from? Guilt doesn't come from the Lord. The Lord will not guilt you into change. He will convict you, but when He does that, He simply presents you with an area of your life that needs to change, and then He will lovingly hold your hand as you learn to make those changes. I don't believe my heavenly Father, who loves me so much, needs to make me feel bad to get me to change for the better. I don't believe that's how He works. I think He lovingly reveals those areas of growth, and gives me what I need to make that change.

Guilt, I do believe, is from Satan. All it does is make you feel horrible. Sure — it might make some people feel bad enough to change. But most of us just feel so awful that we become paralyzed, and nothing changes because we're so weighed down.

There's nothing good that comes from guilt. There are no solutions or answers there. It keeps you bound and tied up, and it prevents you from doing what you need to do to move forward. How much better would it be to follow a healthy eating plan from a place of loving conviction — where you have a sense that the Lord is helping you and supporting you — than from a place of guilt and a sense that, "Jeez, I better undo all the dumb things I did in the past." That doesn't feel good. That's not how healing happens.

And guilt really gives you too much credit: "*I* did this, *I* did that, it's all *my* fault." You don't have that much power! Sure, you could have eaten less or moved more, but there were a whole lot of circumstances that contributed to where you are right now. Food is one thing, but how about all the stress in your life? How about the fact you're taking care of elderly parents? Or that you have a sick child who needs a lot of energy from you? Or that you have to work like crazy to keep your family afloat? It's not all because of what *you* did or didn't do. Yes, take responsibility for your actions. But please also acknowledge that all that was then. This is now. If you've made choices you didn't like before, you can make different choices now.

Paul in the Bible is such a wonderful example: he did so much to share the Gospel, and sacrificed himself to get the message of Christ out... but before that, he was awful! He did all kinds of bad stuff. But he didn't keep himself tied down with the guilt of everything he did in his past. He didn't show up at all the different churches to preach and spend the morning telling people how terrible he used to be. No! In Galatians, he says that he is a new creation in Christ. And you can make that decision right now, today as you're reading this, that you will be a new creation in Christ. Not just the day you were saved and accepted Christ, but today. It can be every day, for as long as you need to be made new.

As Jackie said earlier, God will be there with you, but He's not going to do the work for you. So in order to reject the guilt and start to reclaim some sense of peace and freedom, you have to look at your life and make sure that things are in the right order. God comes first, before anything else. If you're married, your marriage comes next. Ensure that you are there for your spouse — but remember, too, that not everything is about your spouse. You also need to take care of yourself. Once you've taken care of your relationship with God, your spouse and yourself, then you can take care of your children, then your friendships and church responsibilities and everything else.

People get this all mixed up: they put their children first, because those little munchkins will scream loud enough to really get your attention. It's natural to want to prioritize your children, but it just doesn't work in the long run. Yes, they will enjoy being your first priority, and they might resent it some days if you put those other relationships before them. If that makes you feel guilty, consider this: they'll suffer far more if you can no longer hear the Lord speaking to you, if your marriage is falling apart, if your health is collapsing. The kindest thing you can do for them is to make sure you've got your priorities in order. So let that guilt go.

And then be realistic with yourself about what you can get done in a day or a week or a month. This is such a huge issue — we're not realistic about what we can really expect to achieve with our time, and then we guilt ourselves like crazy for not being able to handle it all. Years ago, when I was struggling in my church ministries, because I was stretched far too thin, an older woman pulled me aside one day and said, "The Lord doesn't want you to serve from a place of misery. You might be uncomfortable sometimes, but it shouldn't be at the cost of your health and your home life." Wow — talk about a wake-up call. I thought I would feel extremely guilty about pulling back from doing so much, but the opposite actually happened. I *stopped* feeling so guilty, because now I had the time and energy to really give my best to the things I *was* doing. When you start putting your priorities into order, the Lord will help everything else fall into place.

One final place guilt seems to crop up is when we allow ourselves to start comparing ourselves with what others are doing to change their bodies. There are about a million shakes and workouts and tools and recipes that you could do… but what worked for someone else is not necessarily going to work for you, because your details are different.

The details of their daily lives are different to yours, and that's nobody's fault. It's nothing to feel guilty about. Maybe they have lots of family around to support them. Maybe they don't have to work. Maybe their kids are grown, or they don't have an injury or illness, or whatever the difference may be. You really have to run your own race here, so don't beat yourself up if something that worked for someone else is not working for you. You can choose not to feel that guilt. You can choose not to accept the pressure from the world. Social media makes this more challenging, because you open up Facebook and see that your friend was at spin class at 7am, and then you feel guilty wondering why the heck *you* can't get to spin class at 7am. But it's because your life is different. That's why. And if God's not wagging His finger at you for not going, why are you?

ANGER

In Christian communities, we are very uncomfortable with anger. We feel like because God calls us to be loving and kind, we can't get angry. We know that the Lord doesn't get angry with us, because Jesus has made us perfect in His eyes… and yet we get extremely angry with ourselves when we feel unhappy or dissatisfied with our bodies.

Ephesians 4:26 says: "Be angry, and do not sin. Do not let the sun go down on your anger." In this letter, Paul reminds us that anger is a normal part of being human — God gave us these emotions and we're gonna feel 'em! — but he's also reminding us that we have a choice in how we behave when we're angry. Being angry, even when it's righteous anger, doesn't give us license to sin. It gives us an opportunity, instead, to right a wrong, or to set an example by turning the other cheek. Anger happens when one of your values or boundaries is crossed — it's a warning bell that something is wrong and that it's time to do something about it. So don't try to squash your anger down. It can be a blessing in disguise that gets you moving.

There are two main types of anger we hear about in the New Life Promise community. The first is anger at yourself. So often, someone will say, "I'm so angry with myself for letting things get so bad. I'm furious and there's nowhere for my anger to go." OK — so be angry. Be furious. Scream and rage and yell if you need to. Get it out of your body, and then let God decide what to do with it. In the space it leaves, could you consider forgiving yourself for any wrongs you've done to yourself, just as you would actively choose to forgive someone who had wronged you? And just as you would ask someone who had wronged you to choose differently in the future, could you encourage yourself to choose differently, instead of beating yourself up about it for the rest of time?

The other type of anger is directed at the people in our lives who are supposed to support us, who are supposed to be safe — but have let us down in one way or another. Whether it's a spouse who says unkind, undermining things when you decide to try a new diet, or a parent who set a poor example for us in childhood, or a friend who tries to sabotage us, it's completely understandable that you would feel angry. It's not sinful to be angry when someone sins against you — but it *is* sinful to try to get back at them for hurting you.

When my SIBO first appeared, I was so angry with myself. I was so mad with myself that I had let this happen — especially when I'm supposed to know so much about health and caring for the body! I was furious that I hadn't done everything perfectly before I got sick, and that I was still getting things wrong while I was trying to get better. I was mad that I wasn't getting better fast enough, and that this illness was threatening everything I'd worked so hard for. But soon I also realized that I wasn't just mad at myself — I was also harboring a lot of anger towards other people. I was mad at a friend who had been making some unhelpful comments. I was angry with the specialist for making me wait so long for a consultation, but above everyone, I was angry with my mom.

She passed away three years before I ever even had a twinge of digestive trouble, but I was so angry with her for being sick for my entire life. Why didn't she do more? Why didn't she take better care of herself? Why did she set *me* up to get sick? Boy oh boy. It took a good long while to untangle that one. Looking back as an adult, and as a mom myself, I realize now that she did the best that she could at the time with the resources that she had. But when I was a kid, I just wanted my mom to be 'normal' like other moms. I never acknowledged that anger, I never dealt with it while she was alive, and it took this illness for it to really come out. Eventually I realized that maybe as part of my healing process, the Lord was asking me to forgive her. It took months of prayer, journaling and therapy, but now I can truthfully say that I've completely forgiven her.

And then I forgave myself, for all the choices I had made in the past that had led me to this point. I wrote myself a letter of forgiveness, and it was so healing. Over and over again, I wrote, "You did the best you could do at the time. Yes, you pushed yourself, you had to make hard choices, but you were doing your best." If you've been holding onto anger — towards yourself or others — I encourage you to write a letter of forgiveness. If it's towards someone else, you don't have to send it or show it to anyone if you don't want to. But no matter who it's addressed to, it will help you let go of that anger, to free up that space inside that God can then fill with His peace.

Making that space also gives you an opportunity to see the blessing in what has happened in the past. I looked for what was good about having a mom who had been sick. I looked for what was good about having a digestive illness. I looked for what was good about having pushed myself so hard for so many years. And once I started to look, I realized that there was more good in all those situations than there was bad. That might not be the case for everybody, but how does your situation look through Jesus' eyes? What do you see when you look at it from His perspective?

INADEQUACY

When people talk about a sense of inadequacy about their body, what they're really saying is that they don't feel worthy. They don't feel good enough. They feel insufficient and lacking.

So many of the women we've worked with choose to lose weight for this reason. Maybe you know what they're talking about — you feel like you're not a good enough wife, a good enough mom, a good enough professional, a good enough Christian. You don't look a certain way, and so you discount all your value as a person.

But I believe that the only way to truly take care of your body — to lose the weight, to heal and get healthier — is to realize that you are enough just as you are.

If you want to grow and change, that's a beautiful thing. But accepting exactly where you are right now is absolutely key. It's the first step on the journey, and without it, the journey just doesn't happen.

This is very, very difficult to internalize. If you've believed yourself to be inadequate or 'less than' for your whole life, it's going to take some time (and more than a little prayer) to change the way you perceive yourself. You've been thinking those negative self-criticisms for years, wearing them into your brain like tracks. But God is above your brain and your self-perception, and He already knows that you are enough, that your body is enough. Yes, you can continue to work on yourself if that's the right thing for you to be doing in this season of your life, but if you're showing up in the world, being Christ to people — that's already enough. Being yourself, just as you are, is enough. So take care of yourself just where you are right now, and trust God to show you what comes next.

And you know why this matters so much?

Because if you don't accept yourself as you are now, it's not going to get easier later. When will you ever be 'enough'? What's enough? How will you ever learn to be content? There will always be imperfections. Yes, you might feel better in your clothes if you weighed less, but if you're still constantly picking out all your flaws, your discontent is just going to move onto some other feature of your body. If it's not the weight, it's the haircut. If it's not the haircut, it's the wrinkles. If it's not the wrinkles… you get the picture.

This is why it's so important to learn to love yourself just as you are. If you weigh 200 pounds right now, and you can really believe that you are good enough just as you are, then you're also going to feel good enough whether you drop down to 190, 180, 170… or whether you don't. It protects you from putting all this expectation and pressure on hitting a goal weight. Waiting for the scale to say some arbitrary number to allow yourself to feel joy is too big a sacrifice. God's not asking that from you. He's blessed you so abundantly — and all you have to do is believe that you're already enough to enjoy it.

To be clear, I still have to remind myself of this every single day. I choose to feel good about myself even if my skin is a disaster. I choose to feel good about myself even if I can only eat rice today. I choose to feel good about myself even if I can't do a full day of work. Why? Because this is the day that the Lord has made. I will rejoice and be glad in it — because you know what? Today's what I've got. Delaying my life just makes me more miserable, and Jesus didn't save me so I could be miserable.

PRESSURE

My friend Sean used to say to me, "Isabel, to compare is to despair."

Of course, humans are comparison machines, right? We are constantly measuring ourselves against other people. We start in childhood, comparing our heights marked in pencil on the doorframe, what's in our lunchboxes, who got the bigger slice of birthday cake — and we go on and on and on for the rest of our lives. And while comparison can occasionally motivate us and show us what's possible, it can also leave us panicked and desperate.

Now, we were good at comparison long before social media came along. We compared ourselves at school, at work, at church. But dang — social media took it to the next level! No matter where you look now, you can't avoid seeing what other people are doing with their bodies. Never has it been so easy to become obsessive, researching the best diet, the best workout plan, the best skincare routine, the best healing protocols... but the more you compare your journey with somebody else's, the more desperate you start to feel.

Why am I not there yet? Why am I not better? Why have I not lost more weight? Oh, look at Sally, she lost 50 pounds on the program, and I've only lost 10.

When my skin started breaking out so intensely, I went down an absolute rabbit hole of internet research. I started getting obsessed with other people's experiences — what they tried, how bad their skin got, what helped, what did nothing, on and on and on. And at the same time, I was seeing all these perfect-looking people on Instagram and Facebook — with their perfect bodies and perfect skin and perfect digestion — and I just felt like such a failure. I felt like a fraud and a loser and I just could not stop looking at them.

But then I remembered to put on my Jesus eyes.

The Holy Spirit quietly reminded me that I can choose to see every situation as He would see it, and I can choose to see myself as He sees me. If I am his daughter, which I know I am, how is He looking at me? Well, the same way I look at my own children. I know my children aren't perfect, but when I look at them, I only see the truth of who they are. I don't see their flaws and imperfections. God sees the truth of who you are. He's not looking at your weight or how your pants fit. He's looking at His child, who He loves and cherishes, who He made perfectly in His image. I know it's hard to look past what you see in the mirror, but that's not where He's looking.

Social media has been truly a beautiful thing in many ways, not just for me, but for the New Life Promise community. I have so many friendships and connections for whom I have social media to thank. But social media, and the internet in general, are double-edged swords. We need to be careful with them, because they can easily become a kind of idol in our lives that pulls us away from hearing God and staying focused on what we're here on this earth to do.

Once you start researching something on the internet, you're going to see ads for that topic all over the place, and those ads will chase you no matter where you go! Sometimes it's very helpful to do research and seek out solutions from experts and other people who have had similar experiences to you. But once you've found something you want to try, stop. Don't keep going and going just because there are more articles you could read or videos to watch or accounts to follow. There will always be more, so give yourself permission to stop when you've found something useful, and ask God to help you shut that browser window when enough is enough!

(And once you reach that point, you can stop the ads from following you around the internet by Googling a bunch of totally different, unrelated things. Some of my favorite 'ad deflection' searches are home redecoration, homeschool solutions, vacation spots we could visit — anything that I'm interested in and won't make me feel bad every time I log on.)

I unfollowed all the groups and individuals that made me feel bad — for any reason, whether they were trying to shame people into changing, or just because comparing myself with them made me upset — and I really encourage you to do the same. You don't need that in your life. I also turn my phone off at 8pm, and I don't turn it back on again until after I've had my prayer time in the morning. I know now that if I look at my emails or social media even just for a minute or two before praying, half my brain is going to be composing replies while I'm supposed to be talking to God. And He knows when I'm not fully there with Him, and that's not how I want to treat our relationship.

There is always going to be pressure from the world. Remember what Paul says in Romans 12:1-2: "Therefore, I urge you, brothers and sisters, in view of God's mercy, to offer your bodies as a living sacrifice, holy and pleasing to God — this is your true and proper worship. Do not conform to the pattern of this world, but be transformed by the renewing of your mind."

Your body does not belong to the world and its pressures.

It belongs to the Lord, a gift He gave to you in order that you might bring glory to Him. Don't let anyone make you feel like it's anything less than a precious blessing — no matter how it looks or feels right now.

GRIEF

Grief is all around us in this life. To borrow a line from a movie, grief is just love persevering. It is the other side of love, because when we love deeply, when we have bright hopes for the future, grief is the risk we take. Grief is one of the most common emotions that people in the New Life Promise community talk about. So many of them have experienced terrible, crushing losses, and have turned to food for comfort.

So many of the women in the community have lost children, and I can barely think about what that experience must be like. It makes me want to crawl under the couch and never come out. It's a pain that I can't even fathom, and I understand, completely, how it would make you desperate for any comfort you can possibly get, anything, if it would make you feel better for even a moment.

No matter what the source of your grief, food is a powerful comfort. It's how we connect with each other, how we remember. It's not your fault that food makes you feel better when you're grieving. If you can see some upside in trying to eat well, or trying to get to bed a little bit earlier, doing any of the things that will help your health, it won't take the grief away, but it might make it just a tiny bit lighter. It might make it just a little bit easier to tend to the grief as you need.

Grief knocks you out in a way that our culture doesn't really respect. It's completely normal to have crazy appetite fluctuations, to be unable to sleep, to feel anxious and of course, to be overwhelmed with emotion — even months or years after your loss. There's no timeline for grief, no milestone to reach that will take the pain away. And as much as people might encourage you to move on, let it go, or get over it, there's no going back to the way things were. The only thing to do is to take your grief to the Lord, and ask Him to help you carry it in such a way that you can start to take even the smallest steps forward once again.

Remember what Psalm 34:18 says: "The Lord is close to the brokenhearted and saves those who are crushed in spirit." He is with you in your grief, and He has placed people around you who will help you carry it, if you're willing to let them.

The deepest grief I've ever experienced was when my mom passed away. I could not believe how brutal it was. It took me months to even start to function again. I couldn't get it together! I talked to a friend of mine and told him that I couldn't believe how much it was affecting me. And he said to me, "Isabel, you've never been in the world without a mother. It's not just that your mom died, but that the version of yourself that you knew before also died." Wow. That took my breath away, but he was right.

I had no idea who I was without her, and that realization really helped me start to make my way in the world again. My friend encouraged me to write out who I was and who I wanted to be in the world without her. That process showed me that Past Isabel was, to an extent, defined by having a mom who had been sick for so long, and by how much time and energy I spent looking after her and trying to help her improve her health. But after she passed, her suffering took on a whole new level of meaning, because so many people in the New Life Promise community have been inspired by her story and encouraged to start on their own journeys.

Writing about this also made me understand that sometimes God lets us go through grief and loss so that He can use it for something greater than we can see at the time. I didn't like that she was sick, and she didn't like that she was sick. But there are many thousands of people now in the world that have changed their health because of her story. So He can bring purpose to our suffering, and He can do good with it. Knowing this doesn't make it any easier, and it doesn't make us want to go through it, but He can do something with it.

Going through this process also gave me permission to establish a new normal, because there was no going back to where I was before. That's the other thing about grief — it's not just about the person you lost, but the future you had been expecting to share with them, too.

And the thing we don't often acknowledge in weight loss conversations is that even if you have never lost anyone, gaining a large amount of weight can also steal the future you had been expecting and dreaming of. This is a different type of grief, but profound and life-altering in its own way. If your weight has gotten to a point where you feel anxious or uncomfortable about going out with people, or you sit out of activities because you don't feel able to take part, that represents a loss. Going to birthday parties, church gatherings, family events, travelling, doing mission work and ministry — not being able to participate as you want to each time is a small extra sadness that adds itself to the burden you're already carrying.

Grief of any kind stops us from seeing what is still available to us — the things we could still do, still enjoy. Is it possible that there could still be joy in your life? Could you ask the Lord to help you see things you could do or participate in that would bring you a smile, and a little relief? You might feel guilt for forgetting about your pain for a brief moment, but finding things that you can look forward to, that make you feel excited — it's liberating and it's healing. In my experience, the more you allow yourself to look forward to, the faster your body starts to heal and respond to anything you do to help it work more effectively.

If your grief is over everything you have not been able to do since your weight reached this level, remember again: that was then, this is now. You might have missed out on lots of experiences and opportunities in the past, but that doesn't have to be your story for the rest of your future. Forgive yourself for whatever it is that is causing that grief. Really deal with it — don't just push it under the rug. Cry it out. Talk to a therapist. Pray, pray, pray, and when you're done, pray a bit more for good measure.

No matter the cause, or how long it's been going on, grief is human. To struggle with it is human. Give yourself some grace, lean on the Lord, and find the people who will prop you up and help you on your journey towards healing.

DISAPPOINTMENT

This one is a doozy and it hits women so hard. There are so many sources of disappointment, but there are a few common culprits.

There's the disappointment that the diet you spent hundreds of dollars on didn't do anything, or that you've been working like a trooper to stick to your meal plan and daily exercise… and at the end of the week, you've only lost half a pound.

In that moment, we have to consider God's timing. This isn't going to happen overnight. And there are other beautiful things that are happening in your body as you're losing that half-pound. Things are changing at a cellular level in your body minute by minute. Even as you're reading this book, things in your body are trying to heal. That won't always show up on a scale. But good things are happening in your body, day after day and week after week. Think of what Paul says in Galatians 6:9: "Let us not grow weary of doing good, for in due season we will reap, if we do not give up."

Then there's the disappointment that your doctors don't seem invested in your progress, or don't think you can heal without surgery.

This is certainly a disappointment I experienced with my digestive illness. It took me months, and several attempts, to find a functional medicine doctor who 'got' me and who really listened and understood my experience. I finally found someone, thank God, but for a long time I was so disappointed — in myself, for choosing the wrong doctors, and in the doctors themselves, for not helping me.

The same thing happened with supplements and medications I tried: I hoped that every single one would make me better. Some of them did help, but many of them didn't, and some of them made me worse. Again, I was disappointed every time it was a bust, but since then, I've realized that truly, every single one of those attempts had a purpose. Each one taught me something about my body, and what I as an individual needed in order to heal. Each attempt gave me a new piece of information that had been missing previously, and so over time, I could finally see the whole puzzle and get moving.

And then there's the disappointment that the people in your life are not supportive when you really need them to be.

So often in the New Life Promise group, we hear things like, "I thought my spouse was going to be supportive, but he's not", or, "I thought my church friends would be proud of me, but they don't seem to care at all."

My goodness, that's painful. But disappointment comes from expectation, from feeling emotionally invested in what that person thinks… maybe more than what you think of yourself, or even what God thinks of you. You might know that this time is different, that you're really on the path to healing and change. But we need to consider that other people are doing the best they can with the information they have, influenced by their own traumas and struggles.

The person that disappointed you might be coming from a place of fear or a place of anger themselves. Maybe they're upset that you are getting it together and doing well and they're not. Sometimes people say, "I think it would be easier if I just stayed at this weight. At least then my marriage will be better." But it won't, because 15 years down the line you may have severe health issues that are very challenging, not just for you, but for your spouse as well.

Offering people grace and forgiveness when you yourself

are going through a hard time is very, very difficult. But that's what we are called to do. Ask the Lord to help you offer them the same level of grace that you would ideally like them to give to you — even when they're failing miserably.

Just remember that stopping your own healing because of someone else's discomfort serves no one. You really have to do it for yourself — not because you're hoping to get validation or love or praise from somebody else. You might get that, but you might not. And if you're holding out for that kind word and it never comes, you risk starting the whole punishing cycle over again. So do it for yourself. Do it because God gave you this vessel and you want to make the most of living in it. Look at this process as something you do in a team — you and God. He's the one teammate that will never let you down.

IMPATIENCE

We are impatient with our bodies. One of the most common complaints we hear in the New Life Promise community is, "I should have lost more weight by now." Well, who says? Compared to who? There's no proof or data that you should lose weight on a specific timeline. In fact, most of the data suggests that weight loss is non-linear — it happens in fits and starts, fast in some weeks and slow in others. Your body is going to do what it needs to do, in its own good time.

Now, if you have the energy to do a little bit more each day to assist in that process, then go for it. If adding a walk into your routine each day, or even a few times a week, feels feasible, that's great. If you feel able to eat a little bit less than your cravings demand, that's great too. Going to bed a half hour earlier each night will help if you can manage it, as will drinking an extra glass or two of water each day.

All those things have the potential to accelerate your weight loss a little bit. But if you're happy with how you're nourishing your body, you're following a plan that's good for you, and your body decides to lose 'only' half a pound a week? That's OK! That's clearly what it needs to do to get back to health. That's a sustainable pace and far more likely to stick than if you put yourself through the wringer trying to lose 2 or 3 pounds a week.

Impatience doesn't make it go any faster. It actually makes it go slower, because now you have stress on top of whatever else going on in your body, and stress is the ultimate handbrake on weight loss. When we're stressed, our bodies start to hoard resources to make sure we've got all the energy we need to deal with whatever the problem is — but sometimes the problem is only our own expectations and impatience. The frustration that comes from impatience also slows us down, because we get so irritated with the process that we can make snap decisions that set us back: "It's not working anyway, so why *not* have the cookies?"

If you find yourself in that frustrated mood, walk away. Take a minute. Do something you know makes you feel better, and *then* make your decisions. Give yourself the opportunity to come at the problem from a place of love, rather than impatience. Caring for yourself from a spirit of love, instead of a spirit of spite, fear or anger is a completely different experience, and can totally change how you interact with your body.

Finally, impatience also puts us at risk of missing what God might have for us on the journey. If you can slow down, trust your body to His care, and really start to listen out for His voice, He's going to show you things that might change how you look after your body for good. And if you try to speed through the process, not only will you make it harder for your body to maintain your new weight, but you might miss what He had in store for you.

HOPELESSNESS

"What's the use?"

Do you ever feel like it doesn't even matter if you're sick or overweight? Do you ever think, "Who even cares? Why even bother?"

I'll tell you, I had some weeks like this with SIBO. Mornings are the most difficult part of the day, because I eat and I don't always know what my body's gonna do with the food. One time we were away on vacation, and I was not feeling great after breakfast each day, so I told my husband and the boys to go sightseeing, and that I would meet up with them later when I was feeling better. I tried to go most days… but one day I felt so terrible that I just thought, "Who even cares if I show up? They're going to have fun regardless. They're probably going to have *more* fun without me because they won't have to slow down for me." Oof. That day sucked. It was so lonely.

Soon after we came home from vacation, my entire face broke out after I had an allergic reaction to one of the medications or supplements I was taking. Like I told you before, it was so vicious that I locked myself in my house for a month. I wasn't taking the kids to home schooling group, I wasn't going to church, I wasn't going to Bible study — I just wanted to hide and for the whole world to leave me alone. Eventually my sister helped me find some makeup that didn't make it worse, so one Sunday, the family left early for Sunday school before church, and I decided to surprise them. I knew I had to get back out into the world at some point, so I got dressed, put on the make-up, and showed up at church. As soon as my kids saw me, they came racing towards me, shouting "You're here! You're here!" They were so happy to see me, and that gave me so much validation and so much clarity that actually, it *does* make a difference if I show up or not.

A lot of women don't get that encouragement. They think, "If I don't lose weight, and I end up staying home with just my extra hundred pounds for company, who cares? No one will even miss me. What does it even matter if I get diabetes? Or if I die early?"

I am here to tell you that it does matter. It matters because you have a gift inside you that God didn't give to anybody else. There is only one *you,* with whatever God put inside you as your message for the world. That message might be for your children or your family. It might be for the hundreds of people in your church, it might be for the thousands of people that follow you on social media, it might be for tens of thousands of people if you're a speaker or broadcaster. "The use" is doing His work. God didn't create you as an afterthought — He created you on purpose to be His servant in the world. He only gave your particular gift to you.

If you decide to listen to that dark voice in your head, the world will never get the gift He intended you to give. If you give up, who misses out? Well, your family misses out, your community misses out, the world misses out — and I believe that God misses out, because He wants to see us thrive, like any parent would want to watch their children thrive.

He has a beautiful plan for you. So many times we can't see through our pain to what good might be on the other side of this ordeal. But it's there, waiting for you to lift your gaze to Him, to trust your future to Him. God cares about you. He cares about your health and your sense of wellbeing, purpose and joy. He cares, and that's all that matters.

CHAPTER 5

We've spent the last little while working through many of the big emotions that people feel when they look in the mirror or think about making a change to their bodies. And while sorting through your emotions is both powerful and paramount, so too is understanding how you got to this point in the first place. I'm not talking about looking back at all the foods you ate or workouts you didn't do. I'm talking about the root cause, the experiences in your life that shaped your worldview, your relationship with food, your opinion about your body, and your attitude towards yourself as a whole.

HOW DID THIS START FOR YOU?

Each of us come to adulthood having absorbed specific messages about food and bodies. In some cultures food is deeply celebrated, so precious as to almost be sacred. In other cultures, food is treated like an enemy, or some kind of necessary evil. In some cultures, bodies are celebrated for being big, as a sign of wealth and abundance. In other cultures, the only good body is a lean body, as a sign of status. There are a lot of complicated factors that shape the way we collectively think about health, wellbeing, nutrition and appearance, and each of us brings a whole array of biases, experiences, traumas and blind spots to our own definitions.

That's why it's important to figure out, first of all, specifically what your own attitude is towards food and bodies. What are they good for? What's the right way to interact with them? What makes them 'bad'?

Like I mentioned before, my primary emotion when it came to my body and how to feed it was fear. I was teaching nutrition from a place of fear, terrified that I or my loved ones would develop an avoidable disease if we weren't eating the right things all the time. Even though it's not quite a rational feeling, my emotional sense was that food was the reason my mom got so sick, and that if she had just eaten differently when I was a kid, everything would have been OK. So instead of choosing healthy food from a loving place, like we've talked about before, I was eating healthy food because I was scared.

I've done a lot of work since realizing this to unravel that fear, and to let go of my need to control my food so tightly. I'm learning to see food as a gift, something to enjoy and bond with other people over, instead of something I have to constantly manage.

But everybody's story is different — even within the same family, people can internalize completely different things on this topic. That's why I asked my sister, Vicky, to share her journey with you here. Vicky is older than me, and she carried a lot of responsibility in our childhood. Now, as an adult, the pressure she experienced back then has manifested very differently to what I have experienced. I'll let her tell you the rest.

~

"In our family, there was a lot of expectation placed on me to take responsibility for myself and Isabel very early. Because our mom was so sick all the time, I knew I always had to be ready to step in and help if she couldn't handle something. Our grandmother lived with us, and she took care of us a lot of the time, but if both our parents were at work, I knew I had to help her too.

One day, when I was 10 years old, I went into my grandmother's bedroom to find her when we got home from school. When I opened the door, she was on her bed, having a stroke. I didn't really understand what was happening to her, but I knew I had to get help, and immediately switched into adult mode. I told Isabel to stay in the living room, ran to get help from the neighbors, and then I stood on a chair in the kitchen, calling every number on the emergency list my parents kept next to the phone.

But it wasn't enough. My grandmother died a few weeks later as a result of that stroke. It was like losing a parent. And of course, our mom was going through the trauma of losing her mother, and so that sense of responsibility settled on me, and stayed there. Mom wasn't OK, and someone needed to make sure things got done. It was game time, and I had to take the lead. That's when my issues with food really started. By the time I was 11, sometimes I would find myself in front of the freezer, eating frozen fish sticks out of the box. I didn't know how I got there or why on earth I was eating them, but I realize now that I was just trying to cope with the pressure. I was trying to do anything I could to distract myself and to handle the emotion of everything that was going on around me.

As time went on, food started to give me a real sense of comfort. Before she died, my grandmother and I used to have tea time together: we would sit and have afternoon tea together and watch the news. The time I spent bonding with her was always food-related, and so eating became a way of remembering her. It also became a ritual with Mom — we would go grocery shopping together, but on the way home we always stopped at a Dunkin' Donuts to eat a doughnut and coffee together, or we'd go through a drive-thru McDonald's. It was comfort. It was a way of reassuring each other that everything was gonna be OK.

For the next 20 years, I stayed in that 'responsible adult' mode, taking care of Mom and Dad. My weight yo-yoed a lot throughout that time. I was constantly battling myself to be skinny. In my early 20s I dealt with eating disorders, with my weight ballooning to 270 pounds and then crashing down to 127 in the space of a year. All I ate was canned tuna and carrots, and I hated it every step of the way. I finally moved out at the age of 30, and soon after that I met my husband. He suffered from emotional eating too, and watching him try to deal with his own stuff made me realize: "That is exactly what I am doing to myself."

But we bonded over food, and after we got married and had our first child, my weight got up to 298 pounds. Together we decided that I would have bariatric surgery. I had my first surgery in 2010… and I had my last surgery in 2021 to repair all the damage that surgery did to my body over the following decade.

Let me tell you something: if you don't deal with what's

in your head, no amount of surgery is going to fix your problems. I always joked with my husband — who also ended up having bariatric surgery — that you don't need a stomach surgery as much as you need a lobotomy! If you don't fix your reasoning, if you don't fix your relationship with food, you're going to be stuck in the same old habits and patterns that got you here in the first place.

After my surgery, my husband and I drifted apart. We no longer had food to bond over, We couldn't find a way to connect, and eventually we got divorced. Well — I went into overdrive. I decided I was going to completely change my body. I started going to the gym every day, I was working seven days a week, I lived on caffeine and Adderall all day, and wine and Nyquil-Z and the occasional Xanax at night. And I was skinny! I was fit! But I was also running myself into the ground. I was totally obsessed, and I really wasn't living my life, because I knew that if I stopped even for a moment, everything would come crashing down again.

I had already had a surgery to remove the excess skin from my stomach, and at this point I decided to have an inner thigh lift too. This was supposed to be the simpler surgery… but it nearly killed me. The surgeon used the wrong sutures, and I got such a severe infection that I had to be hospitalized for several weeks. I didn't have health insurance at the time, and so the doctors wanted me out long before I was ready. I remember Isabel praying over me so hard the night they told me I would have to leave in the morning. When she left, I prayed and prayed and prayed, and I finally got it. I told God: "I hear what you're saying. I have to stop how I've been living. I have to stop chasing this 'perfect' body image, because the way I'm using food is hurting me."

In the morning, a new surgeon came into my hospital room. He said, "Vicky, I heard about your case and I'm going to take you on. We're going to start a new treatment protocol today, and I've already arranged with your sister to send you to an aftercare facility so that you don't have to worry about what happens when you get out of here." Just like that. Part of the treatment was to lower me into a bath in a gurney, and it was like being baptized, over and over again. From that point on, I knew my life was going to change.

After I got out of the hospital, I had no choice but to change. I couldn't work. I couldn't really eat. I wasn't in a relationship. I had none of the things that I would usually use to soothe or distract myself. All I could do was sit with God and read my Bible, and for the next two months I learned that I could cling onto Him for strength, instead of trying to do it all myself. I learned to take a step back from my anxiety and to trust that He would handle things.

I always go back to that now, that rock-bottom moment, because I know I'm always going to struggle with this part of my life. It was ingrained in me at such a young age that it feels like a microchip I can't get rid of. When my mom died, I went straight back into my old habit of turning to food for comfort. I lost a friend recently and the same thing happened. When things are stressful, it's so easy to turn to food, to turn to wine (and all those social media memes will back you up on that one, right? "Wine o'clock for mommy!").

But I know now that I can take it to the Lord, and lay it at His feet, over and over again, and He'll never get sick of helping me with it. I know that I have to arm myself against slipping back into my old ways, whether it be with my therapist, my moms group, my Bible study or my daily phone calls with Isabel. Having that army around me, gathered at the foot of the Lord. is what keeps me healthy. You can't do it alone. Even those perfect-looking women who seem like they run a completely tight ship? They're not doing it alone either. It's not possible without support.

After six years apart, my husband and I remarried, because we'd become friends and learned to understand each other differently. Now, on the days where I'm stressing like crazy over my business or whatever it is, and I'm snacking mindlessly and skipping my walks, he'll say, "Are you OK?" And that's enough to remind me to come back to God again, lay it all back at His feet, and start fresh tomorrow.

I'm still not skinny. I still have to deal with my baggage every day. Of all the addictions out there, I believe the addiction to food is the hardest to overcome. We bond with people over food, we get comfort and identity from food, but most of all, the difficulty is that our bodies need food. We can't just go cold turkey and cut food out of our lives. Even with surgery, you still have to eat, and so the thing we have to learn is how to live in the middle. We have to figure out how food can be good for us, and at what point it becomes bad for us.

We also have to work on loving ourselves right where we are. I've worked hard on this, to be able to love myself and let myself enjoy nice clothes at 220 pounds or 180 pounds or 140 pounds. The number on the scale doesn't matter — I feel like I'm starting to understand that this is how I am, and what actually matters is if I am healthy, if I'm doing the right things for myself, and if I'm leaning on God to help me.

If I'm doing all that, then I know I'm doing the best I can, and I'll give myself a pat on the back for that, even when it's not perfect. You just have to do the best you can, and trust Him to do the rest."

~

Like Vicky, many women have a difficult relationship with food and their bodies for nearly their entire lives. Research shows that the earlier in life you start dieting, the more likely you are to struggle with weight gain and fluctuations throughout adulthood.

If you grew up in an environment where your role models were always dieting or struggling with their nutrition and body image, then it's no surprise that you've experienced the same things. If you've experienced abuse or trauma, at any point, then your relationship with food and your body can become very complicated — a way to both comfort yourself, and control how other people relate to you.

Figuring out the nature of your current relationship with food is really important. If you don't go back to the root cause, you're never going to get out of this cycle. You could be 65 years old and realize that all this started when you were 8, when someone called you fat or lazy. Everything you've internalized about yourself throughout your life has a role to play in where you are now. But just because you believed something about yourself yesterday doesn't mean you have to believe it today.

Your relationship with food might have been an all-out war for decades, but you can start to heal that relationship today. What if, tomorrow morning when you wake up and eat your breakfast, it's from a slightly different place to where you were today? What if that breakfast could come from place of just a little more love, a little more grace — just a little bit more like the breakfast the Lord might make for you? You can start to heal the way you relate to food and to your own body so that you can start to see lasting change.

Like Vicky discovered, that might mean recognizing that your relationship with food has sometimes been abusive. That food has not loved you back, and has hurt you over and over again, while you tried to use it to heal a wound. It's about allowing yourself to see that love and joy will not come through food, no matter how good it feels to you in the short-term. In the long-term, food can be *part* of your joy, *part* of a loving experience, but our joy and love come from the Lord. It comes from ourselves, and from the good people around us. Instead of turning to food to help us heal, we need to learn to turn to ourselves and to God, so that food can be put in its proper place in our lives — nourishment and connection, yes, but not the centerpiece of our emotional world.

Once you understand how you came to this point, you can start to think more intentionally about how you want to go forward. You might have ended up here without making active choices about your health — but from here on out, you can start to make your decisions based on the opinion God has of you, the opportunities He's giving you, and how you want to spend the rest of the time He has you here on this earth.

Understand that making the decision that it's time to change and that you're ready will not change how other people react to your decision. You can tell ten different people about what you're doing and why, and you'll most probably get ten different reactions — and you don't need to take any of them to heart.

Some people might be really encouraging. Others might be the opposite and, consciously or not, may try to sabotage you. Others still might tell you that it's a good idea but you're doing it wrong. You don't need to listen to any of them. Don't internalize what other people have to say about this journey. It belongs to you and God, and though many people will be well-meaning, it's time to listen to your own heart, and His voice, and tune out all the rest. The rest are just opinions. If you're nourishing your body in a way that is going to help you do the work that God wants you to do in the world, you're right on track.

I heard a man named Ben Greenfield talk about this on a podcast. Ben is a 'biohacker,' constantly experimenting with his body to figure out the very best strategies for his health. He made the point that if you can spend a few hours each day in the sauna, working out, eating perfectly prepared food, winding down at night with stretches, and never eating anything with a grain of sugar in it, that's great. But if you optimize your body without any purpose, what's the point? You could spend a quarter of the time just making sure you are doing well, so that you could then spend the rest of your time and energy contributing to other people.

That's why you're doing it — so that your body is prepared to love and serve God and other people, without neglecting your own needs and health while you're doing it. The point is not to look a particular way, or so that you'll get acknowledgement from other people. The point is to fully live your life in service to the Lord and what He would have you do.

CHAPTER 6

ALL OR NOTHING

When you can redefine your relationship with food and dieting, you can also start to let go of the timelines and patterns that characterize so many weight loss stories. Weight loss — especially when you have a lot to lose — is not going to happen overnight. It often takes a long time to put weight on, and it can take an equally long time to take it off. It happens very slowly, but so many people get frustrated and quit because they're not seeing results within a few weeks. It takes time for your body to adapt to new foods, and to start to respond to changes in your lifestyle. It will respond — but expect it to take months or years, not days or weeks.

You don't have to suddenly start living exclusively on cauliflower and spinach, either. Going cold turkey on what you've been eating for years is very unlikely to work in the long-term, because the more sugar, salt, fat and carbohydrates we eat, the more we crave them. So if you suddenly switch to eating only protein and leafy greens, your body is going to have a full-blown temper tantrum that it's not getting what it craves anymore. It's OK to move slowly towards a more nutritious and balanced diet. Even if you just change one meal a day to begin with, or just switch out one soda for soda water, that's progress.

The "all or nothing" approach is almost always counter-productive. Give yourself time to make these changes, so that you can manage them along with all the other demands on your life, and so that you don't get overwhelmed trying to change all your habits all at once. Do less than your impulses tell you to do. Do one small thing until it's easy — like one side salad per day, one ten-minute walk, or one glass of water when you wake up. Then add one more small thing, and do *that* until it's easy, and repeat, and repeat.

Slowly, over the course of a few months, your habits will be completely different. Eventually you will have replaced each of your meals with a healthier option. Eventually exercise will feel enjoyable and even desirable. You'll be getting more sleep, self-medicating less, and maybe you'll even be able to explore coming off the medications.

The only way to lose weight and keep it off is to do it in a way that you will truly be able to maintain for the rest of your life. If that means doing a version of healthy eating that is currently realistic for you, that is absolutely fine. Do it that way. Don't force yourself to lose the weight through some extreme method, because none of the extreme approaches are sustainable. Eating only celery and a multivitamin each day for a month will make you lose weight, but you can't do that forever, and nine times out ten, you'll gain all the weight back as soon as you stop. You have to be able to do it every day, for good. We all want variety, satiation and satisfaction from our food. We don't want to survive on salad leaves and boiled chicken. The reason most members of New Life Promise give for their success is that the food is doable. They don't feel deprived. The meal plans include cheese and grains and dessert, and it gives people the psychological space they need to make sustainable changes that they will actually enjoy for many years to come.

Sure — we could make the meal plans more extreme, and maybe more people would lose more weight. But more people wouldn't *maintain* that weight loss, and that's not success to me. "All or nothing" just sets us up for failure. Let's say your child was working towards a goal, and they got 90% there, and then they messed up a little. Would you berate them and tell them that all was wasted? I hope not. You would let them know that it's OK — it doesn't have to be perfect, and now it's time to pick ourselves up and keep going until we reach the goal.

Life is not perfect. You're never going to have all the perfect conditions. Sometimes people say things like, "I was doing so well and then the holidays came/someone had a birthday/we went on vacation and I fell off the wagon." And I say to them, "Oh, you know what happened?" They always look at me like I'm about to tell them the biggest secret they'll ever hear. "Life happened. Life is always gonna happen. It happens every day, so you plan as well as you can, and then when something happens, let it be OK. Just start again tomorrow."

It's not the blow-out over Thanksgiving or your vacation that sets you back. It's what you do about it afterwards. I think most people can follow the 80/20 rule — 80% healthy food with 20% flexibility — which will allow them to be really healthy for the rest of their lives.

Now, some people may need to be closer to 90/10, say if you have a serious food intolerance or uncontrolled diabetes or something of that nature. But regardless of the exact split, nobody ever tells us that getting it right most of the time is good enough.

Let's quickly calculate the number of meals most of us eat in a week. Assuming 3 meals per day plus a snack, 7 days a week, that's 28 times you're eating each week. 80% of 28 rounds up to 23, so your 20% flexibility works out to 5 meals.

If 23 of your meals are nutritious and balanced, that gives you five meals each week where you can go out to eat with a friend, or grab something quick on the go when you're busy, or have something a bit indulgent at a birthday party. Think about that: five times in a single week that you could pick something a little off-plan and you would still be on target. Doesn't that feel more doable than trying to hang onto 100% 'compliance' like your life depends on it?

That even works out over the holidays. There's Thanksgiving, and the day after with leftovers. Then there's maybe a Christmas party, then Christmas Eve, Christmas Day, and New Year's Eve. Over the course of the two big 'holiday' months, that's only six days out of 60 days, or 10% — so if you eat whatever you want on those days, then big deal! You're still hitting 90/10. When you think about it that way, you realize that actually, it would be fine to go to the party and eat all the appetizers and have a drink if you want to. You can still enjoy all the Thanksgiving foods without worrying about it. You could still make the Christmas ham and all the traditional dishes everybody wants without feeling like you just blew your whole nutrition plan.

80% or 90% is good enough. Do the best you can on 'normal' days, and when there's something special, give yourself permission to just enjoy it. You can get back to the meal plan when the leftovers are gone.

3 WAYS TO EAT CAKE

If you go to a birthday party, and there's a beautiful cake on the table, how do you feel? In my experience, there are three ways people react to that cake.

The first reaction is panic: "Oh my goodness, I'm on a diet, I totally can't eat that! I shouldn't have it. Oh no — I'm gonna go to the next room. I'm gonna chew a piece of gum. Don't even bring your cake near me." Almost inevitably, you end up eating the cake. You get so fixated on it because you can't have it. Eventually you've spent so much energy denying yourself the cake that the temptation overwhelms you and you end up eating it. Then you feel horrible. You beat yourself up for the rest of the night, thinking, "I just knew it. I'm so useless. I always do this to myself. Why don't I have any self-control?"

The second reaction is that you don't even think about it — you just eat the cake. And then you eat another piece of cake. And then another piece of cake. And then whatever else is there — even the stuff you don't even like. Why? Well, you already blew it, so what's the point in stopping now? You might as well just eat whatever else is there, even though somewhere in the back of your mind you know that each new food is making you feel worse.

And then there's the third reaction, which is, "Ooh, what a beautiful cake! It's my best friend's birthday, so yes, I would love to have a slice while we're celebrating… Wow, this is some good cake." End of cake, end of story. You wake up the next morning, you eat your oatmeal, you have your almond butter and apple snack… and there's no guilt. There's no overthinking. There's no regret that you did something bad. You enjoyed the birthday party, you had a slice of cake, you didn't think about it afterwards, and your life goes on uninterrupted.

My prayer for you is that this process of learning to address the underlying emotional factors in your weight loss journey will liberate you to eat cake — and whatever else you feel like — with that third reaction. I want you to be able to make active decisions around food, so that you can enjoy your life without beating yourself up *and* still feeling healthy and nourished in your body.

This is surprisingly difficult, because our culture moralizes food very heavily. Apples and spinach are good, candy bars and deep fried chicken are bad. But food has no moral ingredient. We use these words like right and wrong and good and bad, but those words assign meanings to food that trap us into thinking that the food we eat makes *us* good or bad. But food is just food. An apple does different things in the body to what a candy bar does, but food itself has no inherent moral value. What would life look like if we detached from the idea of 'good' food and 'bad' food?

Let me give you an example. Recently we went out to dinner with another family at one of our favorite restaurants. Afterwards, we took the kids to get ice cream. Now, ice cream is high on the list of foods we call 'bad', right? Having been a nutritionist for 20 years, I thought so for a long time. But as everyone was ordering their ice cream and waffle cones and toppings, I thought to myself, "This is good. Getting ice cream together is good. It's nourishing."

We were with some of our closest friends, who we had

not been able to see in over a year. We were having a beautiful time together and enjoying ourselves without putting any judgment on the experience. Sure — everybody got a reasonable cone, no one walked away with a gallon of ice cream, and it's not like we're doing this every day, but if we can embrace our food experiences without forcing them through a moral lens, we get so much more nourishment and growth than we would if we try to control it all to some rigid standard.

HAVE-TOS AND SHOULDS

How many times a day do you think to yourself, "Oh, I have to..." or, "I really should..."?

If you're like most women — myself included — it's in the dozens. We are probably the most over-committed women to have ever walked the earth, and yet we still feel like we have to do more to be valuable, that we should constantly be chasing something extra.

We live in a world where we are constantly exposed to everyone else's life, where comparison is heightened like never before. Even if you spend just a few minutes on YouTube or Instagram — you can Google "A day in the life of... just about anyone" — you get stuck thinking that you need to do more, be more, strive more, have more.

But what if we could let go of the 'have tos' and 'shoulds'? What if we could release and eliminate those pressures we put on ourselves? Whether it's losing weight, or doing something for the kids, or giving more of yourself in some way — we spend so much energy and effort on everything we *could* be doing that we can never fully just *be* with what already is.

The biggest shift in my relationship with myself in the

last 20 years came when I started letting go of my 'have-tos' and 'shoulds', especially when I became a mom. You know the moms who have everything perfectly planned out, everything organized down to the last snack and minute in the schedule? That was not me. I wanted it to be me, but it was not, and I realized that if I was actually going to enjoy my life at all, I had to shift. I had to let go of that idea of perfection and just do what I could.

Working out was a great example: it was almost impossible to go to the gym, because I would have to get a sitter, schedule it into my work day and drive for ages to get to the nearest gym. It was not feasible, but I kept thinking, "I should go to the gym. I have to do more weight training. I have to do more running." I didn't even really like weight training or running! But I had internalized that those were the best types of exercise and so I felt inadequate not doing them. Eventually I realized that doing something was better than nothing, and so I started doing things I would enjoy instead. I would put on a dance class on YouTube and dance around the living room. I did Pilates videos on the floor at home. I found ways to move that worked for me, and it lightened my load.

We also do the same thing when it comes to food and losing weight. *I have to eat bland, plain food that I don't enjoy. I have to eat kale and protein shakes. I have to cut out bread and dessert.* Listen to me: you can lose weight without ever eating another leaf of kale. It would still be effective. You don't have to drink smoothies. You don't have to eat oatmeal. Just because other people like those things, it doesn't mean they're the only option for you. There are no 'have-tos' and 'shoulds' here. There are so many things that you can do to lose weight that it doesn't have to be a miserable experience.

It can actually be enjoyable, and that's a transformative thought.

It's so important, in fact, that I believe there's no moving forward until you've embraced that fact. This journey towards healing can be exciting and it can be fun. The second you start to feel like it's miserable, it might be time to reassess what you're doing. I never want to create a meal plan that will make somebody miserable. Now, will a meal plan require some changes that might be slightly uncomfortable? Yes. Will it take effort? Yes. But this is a time of discovery. You can experiment with all kinds of ingredients and meals to figure out exactly what you like and need. If you don't like something, OK! Onto the next experiment. You don't have to stick at something because you heard it was 'good'. Do it your way. Let go of the 'have-tos' and 'shoulds'. Let it be fun!

CHAPTER 7

Proverbs 31:25-31 says:

> "She is clothed with strength and dignity, and she laughs without fear of the future. When she speaks, her words are wise, and she gives instructions with kindness. She carefully watches everything in her household and suffers nothing from laziness. Her children stand and bless her. Her husband praises her: "There are many virtuous and capable women in the world, but you surpass them all!" Charm is deceptive, and beauty does not last; but a woman who fears the Lord will be greatly praised. Reward her for all she has done. Let her deeds publicly declare her praise."

When you are on this journey towards healing, you're going to have to figure out what strength and dignity look like for you in your specific circumstances. Both are required when it comes time to speak up for yourself, and to draw a boundary around what you want and need in order to heal and thrive.

Strength is a concept we're all very familiar with. It's the ability to work hard, carry a lot, and keep on keeping on, no matter the circumstances. Remember though, that we don't have to just rely on our own strength — the strength of the Lord will carry us much further than we can manage alone.

We don't talk about dignity very often, but it's a vital part of the healing process. Dignity is about having self-respect, and receiving respect from others, simply because you're a human, worthy of care and consideration — not because you've done anything special, but because you're inherently valuable. The Oxford Dictionary defines dignity as being "the state or quality of being worthy of honor or respect."

So what do strength and dignity mean to you? Figuring out how to clothe yourself in strength and dignity will form the foundation of the woman you want to become, and it has to come from within yourself. You have to become the recipient of your own strength. You have to allow yourself to benefit from your own efforts. This starts with honoring and respecting ourselves. We can't expect other people to respect us if we set the example of disrespecting ourselves. It means truly acknowledging our feelings and our needs, and honoring those parts of ourselves — even when they make us a bit uncomfortable. You're angry? Then you're angry! Respect that. Honor where that feeling is coming from, so that you can work it out in a loving way for yourself. That is both strength and dignity in action.

And like we talked about earlier, the woman from Proverbs knows the place of fear — and it's not in the driver's seat of her mind. She trusts the future to the Lord, and so she can laugh at all the wild scenarios her brain can conjure up. She knows that those fears aren't reality, and that they are not her problem right now. She has better things to do than worry, and so do you. Let life be what the Lord wills, and continue to take the actions He leads you to, so that the fears don't have time to take hold.

In his book, *What If Jesus Was Serious... About Prayer?* Skye Jethani lays out a powerful model for prayer that can help us all become the people God wants us to be — both strong and dignified, humble and bold, virtuous, capable and in good health:

Prayer > Action = Passivity
Prayer < Action = Pride
Prayer + Action = Power

I love this. It's so clear. When there's more prayer than action, that makes you passive. It leaves you sitting around waiting for God to hand you a miracle — when that might not be His plan. When there's less prayer than action, that's pride. It implies that you think your own ability and opinions are more important than hearing what God has to say about it. But when you *combine* prayer and action, that's when you really step into God's power — when you start to see what He has in mind for you, and how you can go about bringing His plan into being.

That's the kind of woman I want to be — a Proverbs kind of gal! I want to do what I need to do, without unnecessary worry, trusting in the Lord to show me how to get everything done in each part of my life with the right amount of effort and delegation, action and rest. I want to be able to find joy and laughter in everything I have to do each day, even when there's a lot going on.

My impression of that woman is not that she's resentful of what she's giving. She's not drained by what she's giving, because she's giving as much as she feels the Lord has called her to do — not what anyone else has asked of her — and letting that be enough.

CARRY YOUR OWN BURDENS

Years ago I read a story about a man who God asked to take a wagon and two small stones up a mountain. The man said, "Of course! I'm happy to do that, Lord. My load is easy." As the man started on his journey up the mountain, he encountered several people — some friends of his, some strangers. Each person he came across asked if he could take a stone or two up for them as well. And by the time he was halfway up the mountain, he was struggling, hauling and shoving and straining to get his wagon to the top. By the time he finally reached the peak, he was exhausted. God met him there on the mountain top and said, "I gave you something so light to carry, why are you so tired?" And the man realized that he had taken on the burdens and responsibilities of other people, just because he didn't want to say no.

I think women do this a whole lot. We take on the responsibilities of other people, whether it's in our family, our church or our community. Maybe you say the same thing to yourself that I've heard in my own brain a million times: "If I don't do it, nobody else will." Well, sometimes those things might have to stay undone. Your journey towards health and healing is a big commitment and a big responsibility, so pray for discernment about what is for you to do, and what should be left to others. We are reminded throughout the Bible that the Lord expects us to take care of our own house first, before we try to take care of anything else. And while that obviously means taking care of your physical household, it also means taking care of your spiritual home — your body, your mind, and your soul.

A wise woman once said to me when I was ill, "Isabel, if all you can do is to take care of your husband, your children and your home, that is enough. All the ministries, all the work in your business — if they have to wait, or if somebody else has to take them over, that's OK, and maybe it will even be a blessing to someone else. Don't take the blessing away from someone else just because you feel obliged to keep striving." That hit me so hard. It made me realize that part of the reason I was so exhausted was that while I thought I was doing everything God had asked me to do... I was also doing a whole lot that the world had asked me to do.

Honestly, I think that's why my body crashed on me and I ended up with SIBO. I call that past version of me '4am Isabel', because I would get up at 4am and hustle all day long. It's taken a while for that reputation to fade! I'm in more of a '7am Isabel' phase right now, and even with such a big shift, sometimes I still hear God whisper, "You're a little tired. Maybe it's time to let things go?" Sometimes I listen right away... and sometimes He has to start saying things a little bit louder. Maybe that comes along in the form of aches and pains and generally feeling a bit flat. And sometimes He might really have to start raising His voice... and you can't miss it when that's happening, because you're laid out and can't do a dang thing.

It's humbling to realize, but there's a lot we all do every day that we've taken on ourselves, without thinking about whether it's what the Lord really wants for us.

The only way I've been able to figure out what is from Him and what's from the world is to make a list of every single thing I was doing, and then get on my knees to pray real hard about each and every one. And honestly, I didn't like some of what I heard back. For example: I didn't want help with homeschooling my boys. I wanted to do it all myself. But I heard Him say, loud and clear: "No, Isabel. You do need help." I grumbled about it to myself for a while, but in the end, that led to a beautiful relationship with one of the college students at church who started coming twice a week. My kids love her, she's doing great work with them that I now do not have to manage, and it's worked out perfectly.

The Bible tells us in so many places to pray for discernment and wisdom. And I think that's because discernment and wisdom are both like a muscle: they get stronger the more you train them. Praying for them, then, means asking God for opportunities to train those 'muscles' — which also gives us practice in being really honest with ourselves when it becomes clear that we're putting pressure on ourselves over something He's not asking for.

As your wisdom and discernment get stronger, God will let you know when it's time to put things down and pick them up. If you let go of a ministry, for example, and then after a year of doing His work in your own life, He might put it back on your heart to take that ministry on again, or to start up on a new one. He'll let you know: as it says in Ecclesiastes 3:1 — "There is a time for everything, and a season for every activity under the heavens."

There is a season for everything… and maybe this is the season for you to take care of your health. In a year from now, or two years, maybe God will let you know that it's the season for something else, that you've done what you needed to do for this part of your life, and He's ready to use you for some other part of His plan. Ask Him to show you the season you're in, and what His plan is for you right now. Let Him tell you what He wants you to do each day, and trust that in His wisdom, everything that needs to happen *will* happen. Let your eyes and ears and heart stay open, so that you can see Him and His plan more clearly. He always has it taken care of.

EMBRACING THE SEASON YOU'RE IN

Sometimes it takes some focused attention to figure out what kind of season you're in right now. It's not always obvious, and I've found it helpful to sit down and write out what I want my priorities in life to be, what my priorities in life actually are, and then ask God to help me bridge the gap between the two.

This is a great exercise, and if you're struggling to take care of everything in your life right now, it can really help. Take a piece of paper or whiteboard and on the left-hand side, write out your daily priorities as they would be in an ideal world. Then, on the right-hand side, write out your daily priorities as they actually unfold in your life at the moment.

When I did this exercise, the 'ideal world' priority list was easy:

- A great relationship with God
- Plenty of time to invest in my marriage
- Looking after myself, including my nutrition, exercise, mental health and social life
- Raising my boys as I really wanted to, giving them the right amount of time and attention
- Taking care of my dad and other members of my extended family

- Running my business

But at the time, I was running around like a crazy person, because my *actual* priorities were all turned around. My days were usually more like…

- Business, business, business! Work, work, work.
- Quick prayer time in the morning
- Spend most of my conversations with my hubby about work
- Eat at my desk, race through my workout, take a raincheck on seeing my friends
- Hustle through my kids' schoolwork
- Try to remember to text my family

As you can see, there was a pretty sizable gap between the ideal scenario and the actual scenario — and this exercise really helped me see that I was a) in a much busier season than I had realized and b) that I really needed some help rearranging how I managed my priorities each day.

The biggest issue — which so many women face — is that my entire life was revolving around work, and I didn't want that. Now, you may think, "Well, I have to work! There's no avoiding that one." And you're right. But if you prioritize other things *first,* then God in His goodness will make sure that work fits into place. This is scary: you think that by the time you've gotten through your God time, your spouse time, your me-time, your kid time and everything else on your list, there's no way you're going to get a full day of work done too! I get it, but there is where you've got to be mindful about what you can realistically do in this season.

For example, you don't have to do an hour-long devotional every morning to be building your relationship with God. If the season you're in makes that very difficult, then maybe instead you're just praying all throughout the day, thanking Him in the morning for your blessings when you wake up, and communing with Him as you go about your schedule. If you're retired or your kids are out of the house, then maybe you will have time to do a one-hour devotion, and that will be lovely. But it's more important just to be in communion with Him than to hold yourself to a rigid schedule.

Example number two: your marriage. Maybe you could just be a little bit more present with your spouse when you do have time with them — leave your phone somewhere out of reach and really pay attention to them. Or you could write them a quick note in the morning to let them know you love them. That will take all of two minutes to do, and it can change the whole energy of the day between you and your spouse. Investing in the relationship doesn't always have to mean a whole lot more time from your day — just a little intentional effort to appreciate or support them can go a very long way.

Now, when it comes to taking care of yourself, choose one thing per day that you know you can fit into your schedule. If overhauling your entire pantry to be completely healthy and temptation-free is not what you can do right now, that's OK. But maybe you could fit 15 minutes of movement into your day. Whether that's a walk on your lunch break, a short stretching practice when you get home from work to unwind, or dancing around the living room with your spouse after dinner (two priorities for the price of one!), most of us can find a small window for looking after our own needs.

You get my drift. No matter which priorities you are focused on, acknowledge the facts about where you're at in your life right now. Make small, sustainable changes that will help you start to align your priorities with the demands of your schedule. Don't wait for some perfect moment to arrive to start prioritizing what really matters to you, because that moment will never arrive. The best we can do is simply to start, doing the best we can with the time and resources we have available right now.

When you can accept the season you're in, it can also free you from comparing yourself to how other people are spending their time or what they've been able to do for their own health. If you have little kids, it's not fair to compare your schedule to women whose kids are grown. And if you're older, it's not fair to compare the changes in your body with what younger women are experiencing. Comparison is the thief of joy, and when you compare your situation to somebody else's, you're never seeing the whole picture. They might be in a completely different phase to you, they might have completely different priorities and completely different resources. It might look like you're having a similar experience, but the details are different.

There are so many factors we don't consider when we look at someone else and think, "Why can't I do it like she's doing it?" If God was going to put you on the same journey as someone else, He would have just made two of that person. But He made you into a unique individual because He wanted you to go on your own journey, to have your own story in this life. Other people's stories might seem beautiful — but to someone looking in on your life from the outside, your story might seem beautiful too.

It's tough to internalize this. Human beings are exceptionally talented at comparison, and while that's an incredible gift in some circumstances, we're really not good at switching it off when it's time to focus on our own story. Like I said before, your journey towards healing, weight loss and health is your own. No one will have experienced it in exactly the same way that you are going to experience it. No one else has your past, and no one else has your future. So comparing yourself to anyone but yourself is futile.

Not only is it unhelpful, but it can trap us into feeling like our experience is unfair. If you've been struggling with your weight for years, it can feel unfair to see somebody else drop all their weight in a few months. Or if you've had health problems you just can't get rid of, it feels unfair when someone else recovers with the first solution they try. But God never promised us that life was going to be fair, and I find a lot of relief in that. I know that the sooner I come to grips with that, the happier I'm going to be.

If there's anything that I've learned through my own healing journey, it's that all I have is today. All I can do is to show up and give each day my best shot — even when my best shot feels like almost nothing at all. Yes, I try to do things that set me up for success in the future, whether that's writing out a dinner plan for the week ahead or scheduling a walk with a friend so I don't feel tempted to skip it... but I also know now to let that be enough for today.

And when you can let the day be enough, you can find joy in it too. When you're not trying to do every single thing you can every single day, it's amazing how much joy can start to creep in. Even when you're dealing with major issues, leave some room for joy in the day. Things are not going to be perfect. But they can be joyful, and that's a precious gift the Lord has given us to see us through challenging times.

ACCEPTING WHAT IS

One of the most difficult things to navigate on your journey towards healing is accepting the facts of your current situation. This comes up so often in the New Life Promise community, particularly in regards to family and friends who just won't get on board.

I pray from the bottom of my heart that the people around you are loving and supportive, and if they are, praise the Lord. But not everybody has that blessing in their lives, so let's just call out the worst of it right now: if you have a loved one who is actively sabotaging your weight loss efforts, that is extremely tough and you don't deserve it. It puts you in an incredibly difficult position and it's completely unfair. You're not alone: it happens a lot. We often hear about a spouse who wants nothing to do with a healthy eating plan, and who goes out and buys all the candy and doughnuts and chips so that you're surrounded by temptation. Boy, is that hard.

Not everybody is trying to sabotage you, of course, and it's important to discern whether this person is really trying to get in your way, or if they're just trying to make themselves feel better in a way that has a negative effect on you. But it's OK to acknowledge to yourself when someone is intentionally messing with your plan. In fact, it's really important that you do acknowledge a difficult situation like that, because if you deny it, you can't deal with it. So look at the situation honestly — and instead of trying to fight or plead or steamroll your way through it, take it to the Lord.

The only thing that will change a resistant spouse's heart is the Holy Spirit. You can bash them over the head with this book and as many carrots as you like, but only God can heal their fears and help them see the possibility in what you're doing. That's hard. It's really hard to extend grace and empathy to someone who is making things more difficult for you. But stick with it. It might take days, it might take weeks, it might take months or even years, but if you can model Christ's patience and ongoing forgiveness to that person, I bet they'll come around.

We have had women come into the community and ask for prayer because they're in that situation, and then come back three months later to say that their husband wants to join the plan and they're going to do it together. Yes, it requires patience and consistent prayer, so going to your community to ask for prayer and support is the best thing you can do. You keep doing what you know is right for you, and trust the Holy Spirit to move in your spouse's life when the time is right.

Until then, you keep making your healthy meals and asking the Lord to protect your heart when something hurtful or disruptive happens. God never promised us that life in the world was going to be easy or fair, and we've just gotta work with that — but He's always right there with you, if you can accept the reality of the situation and keep on moving.

The more you work on building love and empathy for yourself, the easier it will become to keep on showing love and empathy to your spouse when they're being unsupportive. Of course it's painful, because you love them and you're attached to what they think of you, but what matters most in this situation is what God thinks of you. Unkind words and disrespectful behavior are not from Him, and it doesn't matter whether or not they believe you're going to succeed this time.

If you can't detach from what your spouse thinks, then that's probably another emotional area that you need to spend some time on. I'm certain that God gave you that spouse for a reason, but it might be because you are going to help change their heart in some way. And that's hard, but you don't have to make it harder on yourself than it already is — if your spouse is not one of the 'safe' people on your weight loss journey, you do not have to communicate what you're doing to them. Just communicate with your emotions and your presence. Let your refreshed mood and rejuvenated joy do all the talking. If you start showing up at events and you're just happy, enjoying yourself, serving the people around you from a good place, many times there's no explanation needed.

Just go ahead, do the thing, and if people start asking you about it, then great — tell them all about it. But you can protect yourself from the nasty eye rolls and cynical comments if you just get on and do it. Tell God all about it instead.

And if you need to have a conversation with your spouse about the food budget for the month ahead, or what you'll be making, mentally prepare yourself for that conversation. Decide that no matter how the conversation goes, you're not going to let it stop you from doing what you need to do.

Start the conversation on a positive note. Instead of saying, "I know you're gonna hate this," or "I've got some bad news for you", just say, "I'm going to be making these meals, do you want to eat this food? Do you want me to make you something else? I might need your help during dinner time if I'm preparing two different meals." Just approach it from a positive place, and don't assume that they're going to react badly. Give them the benefit of the doubt — don't have the fight in your head before it's even happened, because you might be surprised. And if you're not surprised, and they react as you expected, then it is what it is. Again, give it to God, and try to remember how Jesus would be if He were in your place.

And if you have to compromise a bit because this change is going to cause real strain in your marriage, then compromise. A lot of people out there will not agree with me on this. But I believe that when your marriage is functioning well, everything else gets a lot easier. I would much rather you compromise a bit and keep your emotions and mindset in the right place, keep yourself blameless before the Lord, free of anger and resentment. When you're coming from that place, I really believe your body will still respond to even small changes.

So if your husband insists on Sunday lasagna, the way you have always done it, you can make that lasagna and just have a bit less. Add some vegetables as a side dish to fill up on. Have one glass of wine instead of two or three. If that strengthens your relationship and you are loving yourself in the process, I think you'll still lose weight. But if you sit there and stew on it, resenting your spouse and blaming them for ruining everything, I don't think your body will change — and it will have nothing to do with the lasagna and everything to do with all that animosity.

There are so many ways you can help your body start to heal that are not centered around what you eat at every single meal, and we'll explore more of those in Chapter 8.

CHAPTER 8

When I first got sick, I was so hard on myself. Everyday, I would tell myself, "Today's the day! I'm gonna wake up at 5am, do my workout, and do a full day of work." But no. For months and months, that was not to be. That wasn't the season I was in. My body was not in a place where I could push it like I had done for so many years before. It took me a while but I eventually realized I could go gently through the process of healing, rather than trying to force rapid change all the time.

One of the comments we hear a lot in the New Life Promise community is this: "I have tried everything. Please pray for me, because I've failed so many times, and I can't take another setback."

Hearing that plea landed differently for me once I started to experience my own setbacks. Suddenly I could relate in a whole new way: I deeply understood how impossible recovery feels some days. I felt the same desperate ache to heal and get out of this cycle. I couldn't go fast like I wanted to, and it reminded me that sometimes God's timeline for us is slow. It's gentle. It's intended to give us space to heal — to really heal, not just whack a plaster on the problem and keep ignoring the root cause.

I don't want this approach to go in the same bucket as all the other attempts you've made at weight loss. This is not that. I hope it's clear by now that you are not going to find any high-intensity instructions here… just the opposite. I want to invite you to take the gentlest, easiest possible step forward from where you are right now.

I understand wanting to jump straight into the smoothies and workouts and doing all the 'weight loss' stuff — but that doesn't work, does it?

You don't need another 5-days-a-week exercise program or another complicated daily meal plan or any more shakes or supplements. What you need is more time to heal your relationship with yourself, and to work through all the emotions and experiences that have accumulated for you over the years. You need more time with God, falling deeper into His love for you, allowing yourself to trust Him a little more each day, and allowing Him to show you how to love yourself, and how He is going to use your experiences for His glory. The last thing you need is another hardcore plan.

LET IT BE EASY

The reality is that any attempt to change your habits, lose weight and improve your health is going to have ups and downs. It just is, because we're fallible humans, and because bodies are complicated machines that take a long time to adjust to new stimuli, like different foods or workouts. So I want to invite you to think of this as a new journey, a new path — instead of another diet attempt. Forget what you've heard about dieting. Let go of expectations about how fast it's going to happen. Don't hold yourself to the impossible standard of always being "on" the perfect diet. Hand all that to God and let Him get rid of it for you.

Instead, I want you to take all that energy and focus and put it into forgiving yourself. Put it into forgiving the people around you. Give yourself the time and space to fully process the emotions we talked about earlier in the book — and as you do that, remind yourself that instead of trying to change who you've always been, you're approaching You 2.0. You're becoming that new creation in Christ.

Easier said than done, right?

Here's what I suggest: do not set yourself a goal weight. Don't try to lose a specific amount and don't try to get down to a specific amount. Get rid of your scale if it helps (and I'm betting it *will* help — I'm pretty sure Satan invented scales to make us depressed). Instead, focus on the feelings and the emotions that you want to experience. Instead of staring at everything you want to change in the mirror in the morning, stare into your own eyes, and tell yourself how you want to feel throughout the day.

"I want to feel energetic for everything I have to do today. I want to feel happy as I go about my day, feeling God's love with me. I want to feel excited about seeing my friends tonight. I want to feel completely present and relaxed."

If you can approach the day focused on how you want to feel, rather than what you don't want to eat, it's going to be a much easier day. It's going to be a much more pleasant day! If you can detach your sense of success from what you did or didn't eat, or what the scale did or didn't do, you will also be much happier — and I would argue that when you're happier, it's easier to get healthier.

What if your metrics for success became playing with your grandkids, or enjoying a walk around your neighborhood at sunset, or actually appreciating the time you spend preparing your food?

In New Life Promise, we call these 'Non-Scale Victories' (NSVs), and they are an incredibly powerful tool for changing the way you approach your health and nutrition. The scale is just a measurement. The number doesn't have any inherent meaning; it tells you nothing about your health or how you are progressing on your journey towards full healing. The fact is that you could gain five pounds and look great!

The scale is not the ultimate judge of your progress, because it can't measure improvements in your mood, and it can't measure the grace you are giving yourself. It can't weigh your happiness, or your peace, or the joy of your relationships.

One of the most common Non-Scale Victories we hear about is that people feel like their faith has gotten stronger. For the first time ever, they have gone to the Lord in prayer about this specific area of their lives, whereas they never felt like they could do that before. They felt selfish to ask for help losing weight, when other people are praying for dying family members or for peoples' salvation. But God doesn't judge you for what you pray about. He wants to be involved in every part of your life, and besides — He knows that to be able to do His work, your vessel has be intact.

Another huge NSV that people can't even imagine when they begin is that they start to get off their medications.

After my experiences with SIBO, I know that medications can be so important to help manage ongoing conditions, but most of them are not intended for indefinite use. So it's incredibly exciting for people when they can come off their diabetes medication, or their cholesterol medication, because their health and lifestyle have improved so much over time that their bodies no longer need that extra support.

One of my favorites to hear about is when someone is able to participate in some family activity — recently a woman shared a story that her whole family was going hiking, and that six months prior, she wouldn't have even tried to join them, because she wouldn't be able to make it the whole way. But she shared a picture at the top of their hike, and she was just beaming from ear to ear. People surprise themselves all the time. They start being able to enjoy time outside. Their aches and pains go away. Their idea of what's possible for them changes.

YOU CAN'T HEAL A BODY YOU HATE

I've heard several people say this over the years, particularly Courtney King and Dr. Will Cole, and it resonates with me so intensely every time I hear it.

Healing yourself, losing weight, eating healthy food — all of it is extremely closely tied to the emotions you bring to the experience. I know I might be starting to sound like a broken record here, but one of the fastest ways to start healing your body is to really start to cultivate love for yourself. If you are only eating healthy food from a place of fear, then you might not see results as quickly as you would like — or maybe not at all. I truly believe that the emotions we attach to our food and bodies have a huge impact on what our outcomes are going to be.

Think about a kid who has been sick or had some sort of injury or surgery. One of the best ways to help kids get better is just to love on them, because the body is so resilient when it feels safe and loved. The body is so smart. When it feels that nurturing care, that love, it will do what you want it to do — because that's what it's designed to do. God designed our bodies to be self-healing. He designed our blood sugar to be stable, for our cholesterol levels to be balanced, for our metabolism to run smoothly. But when we're constantly beating up our bodies — not just with the foods we eat, but with these emotions of hate and fear and shame — then we're throwing a wrench in His incredible machine.

And the machine is so amazing that it will keep going and going and going, trying to heal, trying to return to balance — and all we have to do to let that happen is get out of the way. To nourish it with healthy food, certainly, but also with the same love, care and generosity that Christ modeled for us. Yes, you'll get some benefits from drinking a green smoothie even if you beat up on yourself all day. But those benefits could be tenfold if you are *loving* the body that is drinking the green smoothie at the same time.

Imagine if your kid or grandkid needed support. You would never deprive that child of a hug or an encouraging word at that moment. So don't deprive yourself of that care either. We all need some gentle kindness every now and then, and we can give ourselves that same love by saying to ourselves the things God would say to us.

Maybe at the moment it's really hard to look in the mirror and say to yourself, "I love you just where you are right now." But imagine what your heavenly Father would say to you. I am certain that whether you are 300 pounds or 200 pounds or 150 pounds, when He looks at you, He would say, "I absolutely love you. I love everything about you. Do I want you to be healthier and feel better? Of course. But that doesn't change the love I have for you, no matter what weight you are... and I'm here to love you through the whole thing." He would let you know that He sees how much the weight hurts you — but that He doesn't see it when He looks at you.

I want to ask you something. What would your life look like if your appearance was not your focus? What would life look like if you went out today and didn't worry about whether people were noticing your weight? How would today feel for you? Wouldn't it be easier?

But we all insist on making it harder on ourselves. When we don't like something about ourselves, we assume that one thing is the only thing other people are looking at. Often, we're so self-conscious that we point the 'flaw' out to other people, trying to prevent anyone else from pointing it out to us. I think sometimes people who are struggling with their weight would love a t-shirt that says, "I'm eating healthy, I'm doing something about it." But you know what? It's no one else's business, and you are not obliged to spend all your time managing other people's opinions.

Many times, when we get upset about our current situation, it's not actually that *we* are upset about it, but that we're upset about how other people see our current situation. You might actually feel OK about where you're at most of the time, but all the emotions flare up when you have a party to go to and you want to look and feel a certain way around other people. Look, again, I want you to go to events like that and to feel great while you're there. If you want to lose weight because you want to look a certain way in your social interactions, that's not a bad thing. But if you get upset the moment the invitation comes in the mail, because you don't feel like you're good enough to attend as you are, that's because you're worried about what everyone else is going to think. Could you shift in that moment to wondering what God thinks about the situation right now? If He were standing there looking at the invitation with you, understanding your reaction, what would He tell you?

Remember that you do not owe anyone an explanation about why or how you gained the weight, and you do not owe anyone an explanation of what you're doing about it. That is between you and God, and if you feel like you know what He wants you to do, that's all you need to do. Remember — carry what He asks you to carry, not what everybody else tries to load onto you. Let it be easy.

STOP STRIVING

One of the most damaging attitudes that social media has really amplified is about the connection between productivity and value. Somewhere along the way, we confused rest with laziness, and now this belief is everywhere. You see it constantly in memes and 'motivational' posts — that if you're not hustling, striving and being as productive as you can possibly force yourself to be, well then you're not valuable, or you're not 'living your best life'.

We've also accepted "no pain, no gain" as a legitimate framework for our lives, and honestly, that's crazy. Just because it rhymes doesn't mean it's true! Pain is a signal that something is *wrong*, not that we're doing something right.

Yes, progress often requires effort, it often requires work, but it doesn't require suffering.

I used to believe that I had to strive and push and grind as hard as I possibly could to 'be the person I was meant to be'. Sleep when you're dead, and all that. I pushed so hard that my hair started falling out and my immune system collapsed, and if I'm honest, it's not because that's what God asked of me, but because I was chasing the things of this world. Bigger business, more money, better house... I was just killing myself doing it, and all the kale in the world was not going to reverse the damage I was doing to my body from not sleeping enough and never taking time to recharge.

What I eventually learned was that there was no contentment in that way of living. I don't mean complacency or just dropping your dreams or ambitions. I really do mean contentment — accepting the reality of where you currently are and being grateful to God for putting you there to help you grow. From where I am now, I realize that it's such a warped mentality to think we have to suffer just to have success. There are plenty of people who have had success and didn't suffer the whole way through. Jesus already suffered enough for us — He's not asking us to go back and re-do His work for Him.

If Jesus was sitting there with you today, what do you think He would tell you to do today? Do you think He would say, "I want you to hustle so hard today that when you fall on your bed tonight, you are just flat-out exhausted and miserable"? Do you think he would say that to us? I don't. Think of the story of Mary and Martha in Luke 10:38-42:

> "As Jesus and his disciples were on their way, he came to a village where a woman named Martha opened her home to

> him. She had a sister called Mary, who sat at the Lord's feet listening to what he said. But Martha was distracted by all the preparations that had to be made. She came to him and asked, "Lord, don't you care that my sister has left me to do the work by myself? Tell her to help me!"
>
> "Martha, Martha," the Lord answered, "you are worried and upset about many things, but few things are needed — or indeed only one. Mary has chosen what is better, and it will not be taken away from her.""

Martha is like all of us who feel like we're never doing enough. She's hustling, she's making food, she's running around like crazy while Mary is just sitting at Jesus' feet listening to Him. We all get sucked into this 'Martha model' — we feel like in order to make God happy, in order to be the perfect Christian woman, we have to do all of these things. But what if He was there in your home? What do you think He would tell you to do? I don't think He would tell you to run around like crazy. In fact, this story is proof that He would tell you to do less — just to slow down for a minute, and let yourself relax into His presence. If that means doing less in your life, then that's OK.

I don't mean to sound negative, or to be all 'doom and gloom' here... but we forget that this life is short. We don't get that many days. So how do we want to spend those days? Completely consumed in this frantic activity? No — we want to be deeply connected to the Lord, to our families and communities — and to feel good on all the days we do have.

God has given you this finite number of days. If you spend those days hating yourself and your situation, how will you answer Him when you get to heaven and He asks you what you did with the time He gave you? Don't waste your precious time, your God-given time, killing yourself to strive as hard as you possibly can. No — spend it doing things that bring more love and joy and peace into your world.

CHAPTER 9

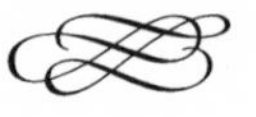

A while ago I saw a cartoon of a woman sitting in a doctor's office with a very obviously broken arm. She's sketched up as being overweight, but the arm is at a really weird angle and should clearly be the center of attention. In the next frame, the doctor is ignoring her arm, saying, "We need to talk about your weight." The woman gets mad and yells, "I'm here about my ARM!!"

One of the most frustrating things in the public conversation about health today is fixation on weight as the sole factor influencing your overall health. It's certainly a very important factor, but health is so much more complex than your body fat percentage. Being skinny or even muscular is no guarantee of health. There are just far too many moving pieces in the human body for your weight to be the sole factor for concern.

Isn't it liberating to realize that you could do a myriad of other things to improve your health... that have nothing to do with dieting? We're going to talk in this chapter about some of the other things you can do to look after your body, and while some of them might have a positive influence on your body composition, they will each have a cascade effect throughout your health that can make a meaningful difference to your day to day sense of wellbeing *and* the more measurable indicators of health, like your blood markers and disease expression.

RETHINK THE ROLE OF FOOD

One of the most important steps you can take to heal your body is to learn to put food back in its rightful place. Instead of being the center of our lives, food should be a secondary consideration. But because our culture is so obsessed with weight, it stands to reason that we are also obsessed with food. Instead of thinking about foods holistically, we think about them in isolation: "This type of food has this nutrient profile and so is 'good', while that food has that nutrient profile and is therefore 'bad'." But like I said before, no food is good or bad — it's just food. It's what happens *around* food that makes all the difference.

Food is so much more than just fuel for the body. It's culture, it's connection, it's memory, it's pleasure. When we isolate foods from their contexts, that's when we run into problems. When we are missing the shared experiences that food creates, we can start to use it as a crutch. We use it in place of real connection, in place of honoring our heritage and culture, in place of creating great memories. It becomes a stand-in for everything that's missing from our daily lives — love, connection, joy, remembering.

This is not made easier by the fact that Jesus didn't specifically tell us what to eat — especially not now that we're living in a modern setting. Our industrialized food environment is about as far from Biblical food production as you could possibly imagine, so it's no wonder that we all get a bit turned around trying to figure out the right way to eat. I don't want to get into "the right way" here either, because I think the right way is different for each and every person. The right way, to me, is when we're taking care of our temple.

That doesn't mean eating perfectly every time, it just means supporting your body with foods that feel nourishing to you. It means feeding yourself from a place of love and fellowship, not from a place of addiction, anger and fear. Once you work through the emotions you have around food, you're more likely to choose something that feels right for you, and over time, your psychological relationship with food will start to transform into something balanced and healthy.

Following a loosely structured meal plan for a period of time can really help start to loosen this obsession we have with food. It makes the choices easier, and frees up your brain to think about things that are not, "What's my next meal going to be?" This allows you to shift your focus onto the people you're eating with, and to start experimenting with what actually feels good to you. This will help you recontextualize food, so that it's in its proper place in your life — an important part, but not the main event.

GET THEE TO BED

If you want to be healthy and feel like a functional human being, you need to sleep — and probably a lot more than you currently do.

We are so, so bad at sleeping in our culture. Maybe you've

heard people say, "I'll sleep when I'm dead" — like their life is way too busy for sleep? Well, they'll be dead sooner than they'd like if they keep that up. For years, I got by on 5 or 6 hours of sleep per night. I was pushing and pushing to achieve more, be the perfect mom, keep my fitness going and all the rest… but then a few years ago, my body completely crashed out on me.

In 2017, I noticed that I was needing more and more caffeine to make it through the day. Now, I'm a good little nutritionist — it was caffeine from green tea and matcha tea, so I could justify drinking 3 huge cups every day, because I was getting all those great antioxidants! But every day I needed more, and then my hair started falling out. For weeks it was coming out in huge clumps, but I just tried to ignore it and explain it away. Then I was invited to go to New York on a business trip, and the night before the meeting, I couldn't ignore it any more — so much hair fell out in the shower that I didn't know how there was any left on my head, and I spent the night crying my eyes out because I thought I was going to go bald.

Boy oh boy, was that a wake-up call. I was fortunate that I had a good friend from high school in New York who was a functional medical practitioner and I got in to see him right away. He told me that I was in adrenal fatigue, and the first thing he did was assess my sleep and my stress levels. He told me that for all my healthy eating and exercise, if I didn't change my ways and start getting *much* more sleep, my body would continue to crash on me and the longer I left it, the longer it would take to recover.

That started my journey into understanding and prioritizing sleep. It was not easy, because I really had to change my mindset: instead of seeing an 8-hour or 9-hour sleep as lazy or indulgent, I had to learn to see it as equally important — or even *more* important — than my nutrition and exercise. Far from being lazy or a waste of time, sleep is a foundational part of caring for the temple God has given each of us.

After all — why would He have designed us to need sleep so much if it wasn't important? Sleep is how your body repairs and maintains itself. Your body is actually extremely active during sleep, repairing your cells, metabolizing all the nutrients from the day, solidifying learning and memory, and restoring your mental and physical energy for the next day. It's crucial for healthy hormones, emotional wellbeing, and weight management.

In fact, for many people, sufficient sleep is the missing piece of the weight loss puzzle. There is now a huge body of research showing that insufficient sleep can significantly undermine weight loss efforts. In a study that compared overweight people getting a 'sleep opportunity' (time in bed) of 8.5 hours with people getting a sleep opportunity of 5.5 hours, researchers found that the 5.5-hour group lost 55% less weight than the 8.5-hour group.[1] That is huge, and it happens for a number of reasons:

- Reduced sleep is correlated with an increased appetite generally, and specifically, an increased craving for carbohydrates
- Sleep duration has also been correlated with the production of hormones that regulate appetite. Too little sleep may reduce the amount of hormones produced to control appetite, which leads a lack of awareness about when you're full (causing overeating)
- A lack of sleep obviously makes you tired, so your

body wants to conserve energy, making you less likely to be physically active throughout the day

This is such an important component of your health and we do not focus on it enough. Just like there are nutrition programs for people to change their diet and body composition, there should really be sleep programs to help people transform their sleep! Now, this of course is not my area of expertise, but I learned so much from a book called *Sleep Smarter* by Shawn Stevenson, which I think is one of the best books on sleep out there. This book will be extremely useful if you know that you're not sleeping enough… or if you're waking up every day feeling like you've been hit by a bus.

After a few months of focusing on my sleep, I noticed some major changes in my body, and in my general sense of wellbeing. I slowly decreased my caffeine intake so that I wouldn't have withdrawal symptoms (like headaches and 'brain fog'). And because I was having less caffeine, I was tired earlier, so I stopped staying up so late at night. If I woke up at 4am or 5am like I used to, I would make myself stay in bed, and do some deep breathing exercises to try to fall back to sleep, so that I would at least have an 8-hour sleep opportunity each night.

Not only did I see a significant difference in my hair, but also my energy throughout the day, and my attitude generally. I felt much more patient with my kids, I was more present when I was spending time with people, and I felt so much happier all the time.

It's deeply understandable if you stay up late at night to get just a tiny bit of time to yourself each day. Between work, family and all your other commitments, you just want a moment to breathe, catch up with yourself, maybe read something or just enjoy a bath. That's OK. Maybe you can just try to get to bed 15 minutes earlier to begin with. Shift the evening forward just a little bit. Over time this might mean shifting your morning routine a little, or changing up something in your afternoon or early evening, but look for ways you can still get some 'you-time' while also giving yourself the gift of gradually getting more sleep.

And if your life is go, go, go all the time, ask yourself: what are you chasing? Why are you filling every minute of every day, long past the point at night when you're tired and want to stop? Maybe you're chasing valuable things — maximizing time with your kids, or throwing yourself into a mission, but again, ask yourself: is this the best way to do it? Is 'more' always the answer, or could your focus shift to the quality of the time you're spending, so that you can step away a little earlier each day to prioritize sleep?

You're not taking away from those other priorities to build up your sleep: you'll be a better parent, partner, employee and church member when you're looking after yourself. When you're properly rested, you're more present, more energetic, more creative and more cheerful as you go about everything that's on your plate, instead of feeling like you're constantly behind, ragged and resentful.

DEEP BREATHS

What do you do each day to manage your stress? A lot of women manage their stress with a big ol' glass of wine at the end of the day, by shopping mindlessly or trying to cross "just one more" item off the to-do list when they know it's time to stop. But this is not managing your stress — it's masking it.

As much as we hear about the negative effects of stress on our health, so many people still don't have an effective way of actually processing and releasing their stress on a daily basis. A vacation once a year doesn't cut it, either — stress happens in us and around us every single day, and going cold turkey for a week won't even make a dent in what's built up in your body.

You don't need an extreme stress-reduction method — you just need small moments of relief on a regular basis. This could be taking a walk outside without your phone or headphones. Even if you're listening to sermons or Christian music, having a device with you means that you are not fully disconnecting. Just walk, breathe, walk, breathe. Or sit in some sunshine with your eyes closed and listen to your breath. Even just 10 minutes a day can make a huge difference.

Anything that makes you laugh and get into a state of flow is great for this — maybe you love painting, or coloring, or making a piece of pottery. Find the things that close off the chatter in your mind and give yourself a specific period of time to do that each day, so that your body has time to siphon off some of your stress and tension.

Stress has a huge range of effects on the body. The nervous system is broken down into two parts: the sympathetic and parasympathetic nervous systems. In order for you to digest your food well, your body needs to be in parasympathetic mode. And if you're constantly stressed, then you get stuck in the sympathetic mode, also known as 'fight or flight' mode.

When you get into fight or flight, your digestive system slows to a crawl or can even freeze up completely. You will not release digestive enzymes, you will not release stomach acid, and so if you're wondering why all your healthy food seems to be making no difference to your body at all, there's a good chance it's because you're chronically stressed. Your body simply cannot absorb the nutrients in your food and put them to use when you're stressed.

Our bodies are not made to be in a constant state of stress or anxiety, but many of us spend all day every day feeling like we're on the edge of a crisis. Whether that's caused by work, a particular relationship, or even by your perception of your appearance, stress is very counterproductive to healing and weight loss. And that can be a catch-22, right? You're stressed, so you want to eat more to soothe yourself, but eating just makes you more stressed… and around and around you go in a cycle of stress, guilt and frustration.

The only way out of that cycle is to lean on God's strength as you find other outlets for your stress. Ask Him to help you find more productive ways of dealing with those emotions. For example, I love adult coloring books. I really, really enjoy them and find they're a great way to bring my stress levels down. Maybe that's a new habit you could try — could you set aside 10 minutes each day to color in your coloring book? Could you set aside some time to go for a quick walk around the block? It might not be your default right away, and it's going to take a little bit of time to form a new habit, but once you've repeated the activity each day for a few weeks, it's going to start to feel more natural and comforting.

At first, it probably won't give you the quick shot of relief that a cupcake would, but remember that stress eating is often a habit that's formed in childhood. Like my sister said, it takes a lot of conscious effort to overcome patterns that were ingrained in you by your parents and grandparents. But a huge step in the right direction is just being aware of what you're doing. Even if you don't change anything right away, just acknowledging your choices can be enough to help you start adjusting course. Whereas before, you may have just gone right to the sweets on autopilot without even noticing, now you might notice where you're headed in advance. That in itself is a big achievement and can start to help you shift in a different direction.

TRUSTING YOUR JOY

If you've spent some time in prayer and rest with the Lord, and you feel Him guiding you towards change, let's talk about what that might look like. Exercise does not have to happen in high intensity gym classes, and healthy eating does not have to involve dry chicken breast and limp spinach. No — change can be a huge source of joy, novelty and satisfaction if you give yourself permission to do the things that you actually *like*.

If you just thought, "Huh? What do you mean, do things I like?" Well, that might take a little reflection. Let's say you didn't have anything left on your list to do today. Nothing else to do, no responsibilities until tomorrow. What would you choose to do with your free time? What would you really enjoy doing? What would it look like if you didn't have to consider what anyone else wanted — and could just do whatever you felt like?

Most of us have things we're naturally interested in, or things that we know will make us feel good and give us a boost. Those interests are a huge hint about how you can start to make changes in your life that will actually stick.

If you're someone who really loves fellowship, you really

love to be with other people, then maybe you could plan to start a healthy eating regimen with a friend. The two of you could get together once a week or once a month to prepare your meals together and maybe go for a walk or do some fun activity together. I did this with my mom for years after she recovered from her kidney transplant — she would come to my house, we'd cook and talk all afternoon, then she'd take her food home with her that night. We ordered meat together and then split it, we would go to Costco together to stock up on stuff, and the whole process was just so much more fun because we were doing it together.

I also love listening to sermons and podcasts. I just love it. I can listen to one right after another all day. So when I am under a mound of dishes from meal prep and cooking, I know that it will go by so fast if I just put on a sermon or podcast to listen to. I also like to dance, and I like to sing (though I'm not so sure anyone else likes to listen). So if I've listened to all the podcasts I had lined up, I'll just put on music in the kitchen, and then, all of a sudden, it goes from being boring and miserable to being a fun afternoon.

The same can be said for exercise. If you just love doing things with other people, then maybe joining a class with people you like would be great for you. If you love the outdoors, what about joining a walking group? If you're totally introverted and don't want to interact with anyone while you're exercising, then watching a YouTube video at home might be exactly what you need.

Any kind of movement counts. Sometimes on Saturdays, I just put a sermon on, and then go from the laundry room to the kitchen to sweeping, cleaning the bathrooms, vacuuming... and after an hour and a half of that, I am tapped! Cleaning your house is a workout for sure, as is doing yard work. My sister loves going to the gym to walk on the treadmill. She can watch a sermon or listen to something interesting — one day she said to me, "Isabel, it feels like an hour goes by in a minute." It's her time, when nobody interrupts her and she can just get in a flow. Now, treadmills are really not my first choice. I really wouldn't miss it if I never used one again. I love working out at home — but Vicky hates it, and that's perfectly fine. We don't have to exercise the same way for both of us to get the benefits. Whatever keeps you moving is perfect.

And sometimes, exercise isn't the answer at all. If you only have 20 or 30 minutes free in the day, instead of bending over backwards to fit in a workout, ask yourself: what would bring me the most peace in this time? If it's a choice between dealing with the pile of clutter on the kitchen bench that is kicking your anxiety into overdrive, or putting on the Pilates video, stop for a second and think about what will truly help you most, from a holistic perspective. Sometimes it's the Pilates, sometimes it's tackling the pile. And sometimes the pile of clutter will only take 5 minutes, and then you have an extra 25 minutes to do something else.

So checking in with yourself is really important. Yes, sometimes you might have to push yourself a bit: if the answer to what would bring you peace is always, "A cookie, some wine, and Netflix on the couch", then there might be an opportunity to reassess there. Maybe a chair workout or a quick walk outside before you settle in might be a good option. But you don't have to torture yourself into doing the perfect workout or making the perfect meal if it's just not going to serve you right now.

If you really don't know where to start, try making a list

of some types of exercise you've done. Which ones did you absolutely hate, and which ones were fun? And if none of them felt fun, did any of them feel neutral? Could you do a neutral activity if you could listen to something or watch something while you did it? Is there some other activity you would be curious to try? Then branch out — forget exercise, and just write down everything you enjoy doing. That might be making art, seeing family, volunteering — whatever you just love. Could those activities give you some inspiration about how you might be able to fit a bit more activity into your week?

The point is to find something that works for *you* — something that you actually enjoy doing, that you look forward to, and that leaves you feeling cheerful and satisfied. Allow yourself to experiment until you find what works for you. Give yourself permission to have an opinion about what you really like and what you really don't. If something just feels like torture from start to finish and you do not feel like you got anything out of doing it, you do not have to do that thing again.

Any movement at all is better than none, so whether that's doing some exercises in a chair at your kitchen table, getting into some housework, going for a walk or putting on a Pilates video — it's all up to you and what feels right for your body at this moment. It might change over time, but start where you are, and give yourself permission to enjoy it, so that you actually want to build this new habit.

~

Sleep, stress management and movement are obviously huge factors for your overall health, but there are many small steps you can take to help your body — many of which will also have a positive impact on weight loss on their own:

- Hydration: your body runs on water. Adding one or two glasses of water per day can have a huge effect on your digestion, mental clarity and skin health.
- Community: loneliness is considered a 'confounding factor' for many health conditions — it makes everything worse. Arrange some social time for yourself on a regular basis (and make sure you get some hugs while you're at it).
- Sunshine: apart from the amazing mood boost that some time in the sun creates, it also improves hormonal function and sleep regulation. Even just a few minutes a day can have a noticeable effect.
- Massage: it might sound indulgent, but regular massage can seriously help your body. It can get your circulation flowing better, reduce aches and pains, improve sleep quality and help you feel energized for days afterwards. If you're uncomfortable with a full body massage, you could start with a foot massage or a head-and-shoulders massage to try it out.

Health is far more than just a number. The body is incredibly complex, and your weight and overall health are affected by a huge range of factors. Yes, food is a crucial component, but there are plenty of other influences. Sometimes shifting your focus away from food and diet — maybe after years of obsession — can be even more beneficial than continuing to wrestle with them.

CHAPTER 10

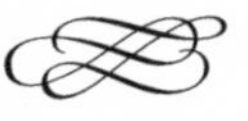

What would it mean for you to trust your body?

After all the years you've spent fighting it, trash-talking it, willing it to change… how different would your life become if you and your body got on the same team?

It would mean peace, finally. Space. Relief. And so much more opportunity to do everything that's good in this world. Instead of hating your body for all the things it stops you from doing, you would be able to appreciate it for everything it empowers you to do.

Maybe the thought of loving, trusting or enjoying your body has seemed absolutely impossible for most of your life. But I hope that this book has made you realize that it's a possibility for you — if you lean on God to help you get there. I won't pretend it's an easy journey, or a fast one. It might take years to get to that place. But you've already started the journey, just by reading this book. You're already on the path to healing.

On the days when I feel myself sliding into combat mode with my body, I will take out a picture of myself from when I was young. I look at the little girl in the photo and tell her, "You are safe. You are fully taken care of. You are perfect. You are whole." And it might sound crazy, but practicing this has helped me heal so many of the fears and frustrations that tripped me up for years. You can do the same thing. Tell yourself in the mirror each day: "I trust you. I love you. You're safe. You're whole. We're in this together." And if you can't say that honestly just yet, say it to God: "I trust you. I trust in Your strength. Thank You for being in this with me."

God continues to remind me that our bodies are designed to heal, our bodies are perfect. And when we give our bodies the time and the space to heal, give them rest, give them joy, that's when real change happens. The stress and negativity around food is often worse for you than the food itself, and so stepping away from that self-judgement is so powerful. Even if your body is sick right now, or in pain, it can heal, if you just give it the time and space to do it. It will heal because our bodies are brilliant, and that's how God designed them to function.

Every morning I wake up to a beautiful song called "Morning By Morning", by Pat Barrett. The lyrics say: "I will trust where You lead, I will trust when I can't see, morning by morning, great is Your faithfulness to me." I can't always see where the Lord is taking me. You can't always know what He's got in store for you. But when we trust Him, when we surrender to Him, even when we can't see — that's when His glory shines the brightest.

It might seem hard to believe right now that your body will heal itself if you just trust it and leave it alone. You might be struggling with some really serious problems in your health, and it might feel like you have to do something else, something more, to try and fix it. This is where it's difficult, and again, this is when it's time to pray for wisdom and discernment. Do you leave yourself alone at this moment and see what happens? Should you keep doing what you're doing? Ask, and God will tell you. And if He doesn't tell you, He's gonna bring someone into your life to tell you. Ask for discernment and you'll find His answer. Sometimes the answer is to just stop for a while, to rest, to listen. Sometimes continuing to push and search for solutions just makes things worse, so give yourself a little grace and trust the Lord to guide you in the right direction, because if it's part of His plan, He can heal whatever it is that you're dealing with.

Whenever I start beating myself up for not doing enough to treat my digestive issues, or I start feeling very anxious about where I am or what I'm doing, I ask myself: "How would I take care of that little girl in those photos? What would I say to her?" And I always say the same things to her: "You're a child of God. He is going to take care of you. I am going to take care of you. You are going to be OK. You're not alone."

So maybe there is a picture of yourself that you could talk to in the moments that you're feeling stressed out. It doesn't have to be you as a small child, it could be you as a teenager or a young adult, if that's when you started to have a difficult time. I don't know if there's any formal psychology behind this, or if there's a label for it — all I know is that when I envision that little girl, and how scared she was having a mom that was so sick, I understand why I get so scared when I'm sick. I understand why I blow it out of proportion when my kids get sick. I have to calm that little girl down and help her understand: "That was your mom's journey. This is a different day, you have a different body, and you're going to be OK, no matter what, because God is with you."

WHAT NEXT?

The journey towards healing can be a difficult one. It brings you face to face with some profound challenges. There's all the emotional baggage that needs to be unpacked, learning how to stop comparing yourself with other people, and above all, starting to trust God to solve this problem more than you trust yourself. At the core of all this is awareness and action. Awareness is simply the process of noticing what's going on in your mind and body, asking the Holy Spirit to give you clarity and insight. Action is choosing what you can do each day, in the strength of the Lord, to care for your body and soul.

So as we come to the end of this book, I want to leave you with some ideas that will help you bring that awareness and action to each day.

At the end of this chapter, you'll find a collection of 90 Bible verses. I would like to invite you to take a few minutes each morning for the next 90 days — three months in total — to sit down with a glass of water in the morning and read one of the verses. Meditate and pray on the verse, then write out three things you want to thank the Lord for that day. Say this prayer:

"Lord, I will look to You today as I care for this temple You have blessed me with. Thank You for my body and everything it lets me do. Help me see this body through Your eyes, and give me Your strength to heal it."

Finish up with your own personal prayer, and then go about your day. After 90 days, you will have said that prayer so many times that it will become second nature to you. It will help you see the opportunities you have to care for your body throughout the day, and it will remind you to turn to the Lord when you're struggling.

Next, make a commitment to yourself and to God that you will trust in the journey He is leading you on. The Lord might ask you to stay in the place where you are for a while longer, and He might ask you to do the work He has given you while you are there. This is where we have to walk by faith, and not by sight. We might want things to go faster, to be out of our pain and discomfort — but can we still do the work He's asking us to do?

This took me a long while to figure out when I first got SIBO, and the Lord had to ask me, over and over, "Can you do this work, even where you are?" For months, my answer was no. No, I could not get on Facebook Live and do a Bible teaching. No, I could not show up to church with my family. No, because I wanted to be healed already! But eventually I realized that God was giving me an opportunity to really grow in my faith. I was going to have to learn to trust in Him more than I trusted myself if I was going to get my life back on track. On my birthday that year I decided that "trust" was going to be my word of choice for the year ahead, and it brought me so much comfort. It helped me direct my awareness — whenever I started getting worked up or upset, I would stop and say, "I trust you Lord. I trust this journey." And whenever I couldn't decide what to do, I would tell myself, "Trust that the Lord can use any loving action for your good, and His glory." Learning to trust in Him — deeply and unconditionally — freed me from the anxiety and impatience I had been experiencing previously.

Finally, if you feel ready to start making changes to your food choices, I would love to invite you to join the New Life Promise community. Our program has helped over 80,000 people around the world to transform their relationship with food. The meal plans and shopping lists are simple, with delicious recipes that are easy to make and stick with. One of the most common reactions we get from new members is, "I can't believe how good this food tastes!" And that's the big secret — nobody ever tells you that a healthy diet doesn't have to be all twigs and berries. We don't ban cheese or grains (or anything else for that matter), and there's even a whole cookbook of desserts. A healthy body can handle most foods, and generally there's no reason to eliminate an entire category of food unless you have a severe intolerance to it. We don't want you to feel deprived, because that's what derails you and it's just not necessary.

But even more important than the meal plans and recipes is the community. When you join the program you also become part of a huge group of believers who are on the same journey as you. My team and I will be there to support you whenever you have questions or need help, and it gives you an incredible support network to lean on every day. Our community is very active, with over 33,000 members at the time of writing this book, and no matter what you're struggling with, there will be dozens — often hundreds — of people ready to pray for you and walk with you on your path to healing.

I really believe that when you surround yourself with a community of people who love and support you spiritually, that the Lord will move and help you start to heal and change your body. Like it says in Matthew 18:20: "For where two or three gather in my name, there am I with them." Well, we gather in our thousands every day, and the Lord is there with us, through all the ups and downs of every person's journey.

If you feel ready and would like to join the community, please visit www.isabeldprice.com and follow the links to the program.

The most powerful changes happen slowly, subtly, even without us noticing a lot of the time. Instead of looking at the 50 or 100 pounds you want to lose, look at the first five. Instead of focusing on the entire marathon, just look at the next few yards. Give yourself time and trust in the Lord to show you the way. God works in mysterious ways — while we might like to go full throttle, He often goes slowly, helping us grow and adapt at a pace that's sustainable and healthy.

I pray that this book has given you a steady foundation from which you can rebuild your self-worth and start to trust God with this part of your life. Take the time to heal your emotions and invite peace into your spiritual life, so that you can start to gently care for yourself in a way that will last and that will bring glory to God.

May you find yourself moving away from the dark and painful experiences of your past into a place of love, hope, joy and optimism about your future — a future where you see the purpose God has for you, know how much it matters that you are alive and well, and where you feel that every day is a gift and full of blessings. May you find the healing you've been searching for, so that you can fulfill the purpose He has for you — to be Christ to other people, and to live a full, meaningful and joyous life in the freedom of His grace.

PART II

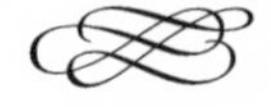

In this section of the book, you will find a playlist for prayer, full of songs that inspire me and help me connect deeply with the Lord each day. You'll also find 90 days of Scripture verses to read through and pray over as you begin this new journey towards healing.

I've chosen these powerful songs and verses for the insight, healing and hope they can bring us. I encourage you to use each verse's page to make note of any revelations you receive about that verse and how it relates to you personally, or if the lyrics of the song you're listening to stand out to you for some reason.

Write down anything the Holy Spirit whispers to you, so that in time, you can look back and see how far you have come with His guidance.

A PLAYLIST FOR PRAYER

There are so many wonderful Christian songs that we can listen to during difficult times. I can't tell you how many times, I've been in a rough place emotionally and just the right song comes on and quickly lifts my spirits.

The list of wonderful songs is endless, but at the time of this writing, here is a playlist I created and have on my phone that I listen to every morning as I get ready for the day.

I hope these songs will bless you as you spend time with the Lord and lift you as you go through your days.

- Blessing I Can't See – Building 429
- Graves into Gardens – Elevation Worship
- Child of Love – We The Kingdom
- You Got This – Love & The Outcome
- Morning by Morning – Pat Barrett
- No Impossible with You – I AM THEY
- Battle Belongs – Phil Wickham
- Christ be Magnified – Cory Asbury

- Faithful God – I AM THEY
- There Was Jesus – Zach Williams, Dolly Parton
- Keep Me In The Moment – Jeremy Camp
- Raise a Hallelujah – Bethel Music
- Reason – Unspoken
- Way Maker – Leeland
- See a Victory – Elevation Worship
- Who You Say I Am – Hillsong Worship
- Blessings – Laura Story
- Reckless Love – Cory Asbury

90 DAYS OF SCRIPTURE

DAY 1

> But the LORD said to Samuel, "Do not consider his appearance or his height, for I have rejected him. The LORD does not look at the things people look at. People look at the outward appearance, but the LORD looks at the heart.""
>
> — 1 SAMUEL 16:7

....

....

....

....

....

....

....

....

....

....

....

....

....

DAY 2

"So then, just as you received Christ Jesus as Lord, continue to live your lives in Him, rooted and built up in Him, strengthened in the faith as you were taught, and overflowing with thankfulness."

— COLOSSIANS 2:6-7

....

....

....

....

....

....

....

....

....

....

....

....

....

....

....

DAY 3

"Get rid of all bitterness, rage and anger, brawling and slander, along with every form of malice. Be kind and compassionate to one another, forgiving each other, just as in Christ God forgave you."

— EPHESIANS 4:31-32

....

....

....

....

....

....

....

....

....

....

....

....

....

....

....

BIBLE VERSES 4

DAY 4

"Therefore, my dear brothers and sisters, stand firm. Let nothing move you. Always give yourselves fully to the work of the LORD, because you know that your labor in the LORD is not in vain."

— 1 CORINTHIANS 15:58

BIBLE VERSES 5

DAY 5

> "But rejoice in as much as you participate in the sufferings of Christ, so that you may be overjoyed when His glory is revealed."
>
> — 1 PETER 4:13

....

....

....

....

....

....

....

....

....

....

....

....

....

....

....

....

BIBLE VERSES 6

DAY 6

"Because of the LORD's great love we are not consumed, for His compassions never fails. They are new every morning; great is Your faithfulness."

— LAMENTATIONS 3:22-23

....
....
....
....
....
....
....
....
....
....
....
....
....
....
....
....

DAY 7

"Worship the LORD your God, and His blessing will be on your food and water. I will take away sickness from among you."

— EXODUS 23:25

....

....

....

....

....

....

....

....

....

....

....

....

....

....

....

....

DAY 8

"Trust in the LORD with all your heart and lean not on your own understanding; in all your ways submit to Him, and He will make your paths straight."

— PROVERBS 3:5-6

....

....

....

....

....

....

....

....

....

....

....

....

....

....

....

....

DAY 9

"Then they cried to the LORD in their trouble, and He saved them from their distress. He sent out His word and healed them; He rescued them from the grave. Let them give thanks to the LORD for His unfailing love and His wonderful deeds for mankind."

— PSALM 107:19-21

....

....

....

....

....

....

....

....

....

....

....

....

....

....

DAY 10

"When I am in distress, I call to You, because You answer me."

— PSALM 86:7

....
....
....
....
....
....
....
....
....
....
....
....
....
....
....
....
....

DAY 11

"If any of you lacks wisdom, you should ask God, who gives generously to all without finding fault, and it will be given to you. But when you ask, you must believe and not doubt, because the one who doubts is like a wave of the sea, blown and tossed by the wind."

— JAMES 1:5-6

....

....

....

....

....

....

....

....

....

....

....

....

....

....

DAY 12

"Look to the LORD and His strength; seek His face always."

—1 CHRONICLES 16:11

....

....

....

....

....

....

....

....

....

....

....

....

....

....

....

....

....

....

DAY 13

"The LORD is my rock, my fortress and my deliverer; my God is my rock, in whom I take refuge, my shield and the horn of my salvation, my stronghold."

— PSALM 18:2

....

....

....

....

....

....

....

....

....

....

....

....

....

....

....

....

DAY 14

"Taste and see that the LORD is good; blessed is the one who takes refuge in Him."

— PSALM 34:8

....

....

....

....

....

....

....

....

....

....

....

....

....

....

....

....

....

DAY 15

"So do not worry, saying, 'What shall we eat?' or 'What shall we drink?' or 'What shall we wear?' For the pagans run after all these things, and your heavenly Father knows that you need them. But seek first His kingdom and His righteousness, and all these things will be given to you as well. Therefore do not worry about tomorrow, for tomorrow will worry about itself. Each day has enough trouble of its own."

— MATTHEW 6:31-34

....

....

....

....

....

....

....

....

....

....

....

DAY 16

"For the Spirit God gave us does not make us timid, but gives us power, love and self-discipline."

— 2 TIMOTHY 1:7

....

....

....

....

....

....

....

....

....

....

....

....

....

....

....

....

....

DAY 17

"But He said to me, "My grace is sufficient for you, for my power is made perfect in weakness." Therefore I will boast all the more gladly about my weaknesses, so that Christ's power may rest on me."

— 2 CORINTHIANS 12:9

DAY 18

"May the God of hope fill you with all joy and peace as you trust in Him, so that you may overflow with hope by the power of the Holy Spirit."

— ROMANS 15:13

DAY 19

"He gives strength to the weary and increases the power of the weak."

— ISAIAH 40:29

DAY 20

"Therefore, if anyone is in Christ, the new creation has come: The old has gone, the new is here!"

— 2 CORINTHIANS 5:17

....

....

....

....

....

....

....

....

....

....

....

....

....

....

....

....

....

DAY 21

"You did not choose me, but I chose you and appointed you so that you might go and bear fruit — fruit that will last — and so that whatever you ask in my name the Father will give you."

— JOHN 15:16

....

....

....

....

....

....

....

....

....

....

....

....

....

....

....

DAY 22

"No temptation has overtaken you except what is common to mankind. And God is faithful; He will not let you be tempted beyond what you can bear. But when you are tempted, He will also provide a way out so that you can endure it."

— 1 CORINTHIANS 10:3

DAY 23

"LORD, by such things people live; and my spirit finds life in them too. You restored me to health and let me live. Surely it was for my benefit that I suffered such anguish. In Your love you kept me from the pit of destruction; You have put all my sins behind Your back."

— ISAIAH 38:16-17

....

....

....

....

....

....

....

....

....

....

....

....

....

....

DAY 24

"'For I know the plans I have for you,' declares the LORD, 'plans to prosper you and not to harm you, plans to give you hope and a future.'"

— JEREMIAH 29:11

DAY 25

"And my God will meet all your needs according to the riches of his glory in Christ Jesus."

— PHILIPPIANS 4:19

....

....

....

....

....

....

....

....

....

....

....

....

....

....

....

....

DAY 26

"I have told you this so that My joy may be in you and that your joy may be complete."

— JOHN 15:11

....
....
....
....
....
....
....
....
....
....
....
....
....
....
....
....
....

DAY 27

"And we know that in all things God works for the good of those who love Him, who have been called according to His purpose."

— ROMANS 8:28

....

....

....

....

....

....

....

....

....

....

....

....

....

....

....

....

DAY 28

"I praise You because I am fearfully and wonderfully made; Your works are wonderful, I know that full well."

— PSALM 139:14

....

....

....

....

....

....

....

....

....

....

....

....

....

....

....

....

....

DAY 29

"My flesh and my heart may fail, but God is the strength of my heart and my portion forever."

— PSALM 73:26

DAY 30

"God is our refuge and strength, an ever-present help in trouble. Therefore we will not fear, though the earth give way and the mountains fall into the heart of the sea, though its waters roar and foam and the mountains quake with their surging."

— PSALM 46:1-3

....

....

....

....

....

....

....

....

....

....

....

....

....

....

DAY 31

"Humble yourselves, therefore, under God's mighty hand, that He may lift you up in due time. Cast all your anxiety on Him because he cares for you."

— 1 PETER 5:6-7

....

....

....

....

....

....

....

....

....

....

....

....

....

....

....

....

DAY 32

"Who of you by worrying can add a single hour to your life? Since you cannot do this very little thing, why do you worry about the rest?"

— LUKE 12:25-26

DAY 33

"For I am the LORD your God who takes hold of your right hand and says to you, "Do not fear; I will help you.""

— ISAIAH 41:13

....

....

....

....

....

....

....

....

....

....

....

....

....

....

....

....

....

DAY 34

"Have I not commanded you? Be strong and courageous. Do not be afraid; do not be discouraged, for the LORD your God will be with you wherever you go."

— JOSHUA 1:9

DAY 35

"Peace I leave with you; My peace I give you. I do not give to you as the world gives. Do not let your hearts be troubled and do not be afraid."

— JOHN 14:27

....

....

....

....

....

....

....

....

....

....

....

....

....

....

....

....

DAY 36

"Do not be anxious about anything, but in every situation, by prayer and petition, with thanksgiving, present your requests to God. And the peace of God, which transcends all understanding, will guard your hearts and your minds in Christ Jesus."

— PHILIPPIANS 4:6-7

....

....

....

....

....

....

....

....

....

....

....

....

....

....

DAY 37

"I keep my eyes always on the Lord. With Him at my right hand, I will not be shaken. Therefore my heart is glad and my tongue rejoices; my body also will rest secure."

— PSALM 16:8-9

....
....
....
....
....
....
....
....
....
....
....
....
....
....
....
....

DAY 38

"A cheerful heart is good medicine, but a crushed spirit dries up the bones."

— PROVERBS 17:22

....
....
....
....
....
....
....
....
....
....
....
....
....
....
....
....

DAY 39

"He will wipe every tear from their eyes. There will be no more death or mourning or crying or pain, for the old order of things has passed away."

— REVELATION 21:4

....
....
....
....
....
....
....
....
....
....
....
....
....
....
....
....

DAY 40

"The LORD is my light and my salvation — whom shall I fear? The LORD is the stronghold of my life — of whom shall I be afraid?"

— PSALM 27:1

....

....

....

....

....

....

....

....

....

....

....

....

....

....

....

....

DAY 41

"If My people, who are called by My name, will humble themselves and pray and seek My face and turn from their wicked ways, then I will hear from heaven, and I will forgive their sin and will heal their land."

— 2 CHRONICLES 7:14

....

....

....

....

....

....

....

....

....

....

....

....

....

....

....

DAY 42

"Walk in obedience to all that the LORD your God has commanded you, so that you may live and prosper and prolong your days in the land that you will possess."

— DEUTERONOMY 5:33

DAY 43

"If we confess our sins, He is faithful and just and will forgive us our sins and purify us from all unrighteousness."

— 1 JOHN 1:9

....

....

....

....

....

....

....

....

....

....

....

....

....

....

....

....

....

DAY 44

"Therefore, since we are surrounded by such a great cloud of witnesses, let us throw off everything that hinders and the sin that so easily entangles. And let us run with perseverance the race marked out for us, fixing our eyes on Jesus, the pioneer and perfecter of faith. For the joy set before Him He endured the cross, scorning its shame, and sat down at the right hand of the throne of God."

— HEBREWS 12:1-2

....

....

....

....

....

....

....

....

....

....

....

....

DAY 45

"Do nothing out of selfish ambition or vain conceit. Rather, in humility value others above yourselves, not looking to your own interests but each of you to the interests of the others."

— PHILIPPIANS 2:3-4

....

....

....

....

....

....

....

....

....

....

....

....

....

....

....

DAY 46

"Therefore everyone who hears these words of Mine and puts them into practice is like a wise man who built his house on the rock."

— MATTHEW 7:24

....

....

....

....

....

....

....

....

....

....

....

....

....

....

....

....

DAY 47

"And when you stand praying, if you hold anything against anyone, forgive them, so that your Father in heaven may forgive you your sins."

— MARK 11:25-26

....

....

....

....

....

....

....

....

....

....

....

....

....

....

....

....

DAY 48

"Therefore confess your sins to each other and pray for each other so that you may be healed. The prayer of a righteous person is powerful and effective."

— JAMES 5:16

DAY 49

"My son, pay attention to what I say; turn your ear to my words. Do not let them out of your sight, keep them within your heart; for they are life to those who find them and health to one's whole body."

— PROVERBS 4:20-22

....

....

....

....

....

....

....

....

....

....

....

....

....

....

....

DAY 50

"Do not conform to the pattern of this world, but be transformed by the renewing of your mind. Then you will be able to test and approve what God's will is — His good, pleasing and perfect will."

— ROMANS 12:2

....

....

....

....

....

....

....

....

....

....

....

....

....

....

....

DAY 51

"Commit to the LORD whatever you do, and He will establish your plans."

— PROVERBS 16:3

....

....

....

....

....

....

....

....

....

....

....

....

....

....

....

....

....

DAY 52

"Hear, LORD, and be merciful to me; LORD, be my help. You turned my wailing into dancing; You removed my sackcloth and clothed me with joy."

— PSALM 30:10-11

DAY 53

"Heal me, LORD, and I will be healed; save me and I will be saved, for You are the one I praise."

— JEREMIAH 17:14

DAY 54

"Have mercy on me, LORD, for I am faint; heal me, LORD, for my bones are in agony."

— PSALM 6:2

DAY 55

"Dear friend, I pray that you may enjoy good health and that all may go well with you, even as your soul is getting along well."

— 3 JOHN 1:2

....

....

....

....

....

....

....

....

....

....

....

....

....

....

....

....

DAY 56

“On hearing this, Jesus said to them, “It is not the healthy who need a doctor, but the sick. I have not come to call the righteous, but sinners.””

— MARK 2:17

....

....

....

....

....

....

....

....

....

....

....

....

....

....

....

....

DAY 57

> "But I will restore you to health and heal your wounds," declares the LORD."
>
> — JEREMIAH 30:17

DAY 58

"Is anyone among you sick? Let them call the elders of the church to pray over them and anoint them with oil in the name of the LORD. And the prayer offered in faith will make the sick person well; the LORD will raise them up. If they have sinned, they will be forgiven."

— JAMES 5:14-15

....

....

....

....

....

....

....

....

....

....

....

....

....

....

DAY 59

"Jesus went through all the towns and villages, teaching in their synagogues, proclaiming the good news of the kingdom and healing every disease and sickness."

— MATTHEW 9:35

....

....

....

....

....

....

....

....

....

....

....

....

....

....

....

....

DAY 60

"When I said, "My foot is slipping," Your unfailing love, LORD, supported me. When anxiety was great within me, Your consolation brought me joy."

— PSALM 94:18-19

....

....

....

....

....

....

....

....

....

....

....

....

....

....

....

....

DAY 61

"Nevertheless, I will bring health and healing to it; I will heal My people and will let them enjoy abundant peace and security."

— JEREMIAH 33:6

....

....

....

....

....

....

....

....

....

....

....

....

....

....

....

....

DAY 62

"See now that I myself am He! There is no god besides Me. I put to death and I bring to life, I have wounded and I will heal, and no one can deliver out of My hand."

— DEUTERONOMY 32:39

DAY 63

"The LORD himself goes before you and will be with you; He will never leave you nor forsake you. Do not be afraid; do not be discouraged."

— DEUTERONOMY 31:8

....

....

....

....

....

....

....

....

....

....

....

....

....

....

....

....

DAY 64

"Once, on being asked by the Pharisees when the kingdom of God would come, Jesus replied, "The coming of the kingdom of God is not something that can be observed, nor will people say, 'Here it is,' or 'There it is,' because the kingdom of God is in your midst.""

— LUKE 17:20-21

....

....

....

....

....

....

....

....

....

....

....

....

....

....

DAY 65

"I have been crucified with Christ and I no longer live, but Christ lives in me. The life I now live in the body, I live by faith in the Son of God, who loved me and gave Himself for me."

— GALATIANS 2:20

DAY 66

"Therefore, I urge you, brothers and sisters, in view of God's mercy, to offer your bodies as a living sacrifice, holy and pleasing to God — this is your true and proper worship."

— ROMANS 12:1

....

....

....

....

....

....

....

....

....

....

....

....

....

....

....

....

DAY 67

"The LORD is my strength and my defense; He has become my salvation. He is my God, and I will praise Him, my father's God, and I will exalt Him."

— EXODUS 15:2

....

....

....

....

....

....

....

....

....

....

....

....

....

....

....

....

DAY 68

"So do not fear, for I am with you; do not be dismayed, for I am your God. I will strengthen you and help you; I will uphold you with my righteous right hand."

— ISAIAH 41:10

....

....

....

....

....

....

....

....

....

....

....

....

....

....

....

....

DAY 69

"My son, do not forget my teaching, but keep my commands in your heart, for they will prolong your life many years and bring you peace and prosperity."

— PROVERBS 3:1-2

DAY 70

"He says, "Be still, and know that I am God; I will be exalted among the nations, I will be exalted in the earth.""

— PSALM 46:10

....

....

....

....

....

....

....

....

....

....

....

....

....

....

....

....

....

DAY 71

"I have told you these things, so that in Me you may have peace. In this world you will have trouble. But take heart! I have overcome the world."

— JOHN 16:33

....

....

....

....

....

....

....

....

....

....

....

....

....

....

....

....

DAY 72

"I sought the LORD, and He answered me; He delivered me from all my fears. Those who look to Him are radiant; their faces are never covered with shame."

— PSALM 34:4-5

DAY 73

"The grass withers and the flowers fall, but the word of our God endures forever."

— ISAIAH 40:8

....
....
....
....
....
....
....
....
....
....
....
....
....
....
....
....
....

DAY 74

"LORD, be gracious to us; we long for You. Be our strength every morning, our salvation in time of distress."

— ISAIAH 33:2

....

....

....

....

....

....

....

....

....

....

....

....

....

....

....

....

....

DAY 75

"The LORD replied, 'My Presence will go with you, and I will give you rest.'"

— EXODUS 33:14

....
....
....
....
....
....
....
....
....
....
....
....
....
....
....
....
....

DAY 76

"Be strong and take heart, all you who hope in the LORD."

— PSALM 31:24

....

....

....

....

....

....

....

....

....

....

....

....

....

....

....

....

....

....

DAY 77

"I am not saying this because I am in need, for I have learned to be content whatever the circumstances. I know what it is to be in need, and I know what it is to have plenty. I have learned the secret of being content in any and every situation, whether well fed or hungry, whether living in plenty or in want."

— PHILIPPIANS 4:11-12

....

....

....

....

....

....

....

....

....

....

....

....

....

DAY 78

"Come to Me, all you who are weary and burdened, and I will give you rest. Take My yoke upon you and learn from me, for I am gentle and humble in heart, and you will find rest for your souls. For My yoke is easy and my burden is light."

— MATTHEW 11:28-30

DAY 79

"Therefore confess your sins to each other and pray for each other so that you may be healed. The prayer of a righteous person is powerful and effective."

— JAMES 5:13

DAY 80

"Praise the LORD, my soul, and forget not all His benefits — who forgives all your sins and heals all your diseases, who redeems your life from the pit and crowns you with love and compassion."

— PSALM 103:2-4

....

....

....

....

....

....

....

....

....

....

....

....

....

....

....

DAY 81

"The name of the LORD is a fortified tower; the righteous run to it and are safe."

— PROVERBS 18:10

....

....

....

....

....

....

....

....

....

....

....

....

....

....

....

....

....

DAY 82

"You will keep in perfect peace those whose minds are steadfast, because they trust in You."

— ISAIAH 26:3

....

....

....

....

....

....

....

....

....

....

....

....

....

....

....

....

....

DAY 83

"Whoever heeds discipline shows the way to life, but whoever ignores correction leads others astray."

— PROVERBS 10:17

....
....
....
....
....
....
....
....
....
....
....
....
....
....
....
....
....

DAY 84

"Now faith is confidence in what we hope for and assurance about what we do not see."

— HEBREWS 11:1

....

....

....

....

....

....

....

....

....

....

....

....

....

....

....

....

....

DAY 85

"Consider it pure joy, my brothers and sisters, whenever you face trials of many kinds, because you know that the testing of your faith produces perseverance."

— JAMES 1:2-3

DAY 86

"In the morning, LORD, you hear my voice; in the morning I lay my requests before You and wait expectantly."

— PSALM 5:3

....

....

....

....

....

....

....

....

....

....

....

....

....

....

....

....

....

DAY 87

"Therefore, since we have been justified through faith, we have peace with God through our LORD Jesus Christ, through whom we have gained access by faith into this grace in which we now stand. And we boast in the hope of the glory of God."

— ROMANS 5:1-2

....

....

....

....

....

....

....

....

....

....

....

....

....

....

DAY 88

"I will lead the blind by ways they have not known, along unfamiliar paths I will guide them; I will turn the darkness into light before them and make the rough places smooth. These are the things I will do; I will not forsake them."

— ISAIAH 42:16

DAY 89

"Now to Him who is able to do immeasurably more than all we ask or imagine, according to His power that is at work within us."

— EPHESIANS 3:20

....

....

....

....

....

....

....

....

....

....

....

....

....

....

....

....

DAY 90

"Let the morning bring me word of Your unfailing love, for I have put my trust in You. Show me the way I should go, for to You I entrust my life."

— PSALMS 143:8

NOTES

CHAPTER 9

1. *Annals of Internal Medicine,* 2010 Oct 5; 153(7): 435–441. Arlet V. Nedeltcheva, MD, et al. "Insufficient sleep undermines dietary efforts to reduce adiposity." https://www.ncbi.nlm.nih.gov/pmc/articles/PMC2951287/

Made in United States
Orlando, FL
02 September 2023